This book is dedicated to
everyone whose body has
been used by science.

Burke – Now and then

Janet Philp

Published by Anatomy Fundamentals

First published by Anatomy Fundamentals 2016
47 Liberton Gardens, Edinburgh EH16 6JT

ISBN 978-0-9955101-0-4

Published by Anatomy Fundamentals
Printed in the UK by Printing@ed.ac.uk

Acknowledgements

As with any production there are many people to thank.

I need to thank my family who have been supportive during this obsession with a serial killer. They probably know more about William Burke than they will ever need to.

I need to thank my colleagues in the Anatomy Department without whose support and encouragement my interest in all things anatomical might have waned.

I need to thank the people in all of the archives and special collection departments that I have consulted both within the University, Edinburgh, London and the numerous Royal Colleges and Societies without whose expert knowledge this volume would have taken much longer to produce. I need to thank various colleagues in numerous places who have offered advice and assistance on many things from genealogy to the pathology of testicular cancer and facial reconstructions. Thank you for fielding what must have appeared to be very strange questions at the time.

Lastly I suppose I should note David Boyle, without whose ruling we would not have the skeleton of William Burke, which inspired the whole volume.

Preface

As an anatomist at the University of Edinburgh, it is very hard to escape the legacy of Burke and Hare. Although it is nearly 200 hundred years since Burke and Hare went on their murdering spree, the fascination that the public has for these notorious characters has not waned. Plays and films have been made about them and numerous books written about their exploits all with varying degrees of accuracy; in some cases there is no documentary evidence to support the speculative statements made in some of the books written about them.

This however cannot be said of this account of the Burke and Hare story. In an entirely novel approach, Janet Philp very cleverly retells the 'story' of Burke and Hare from Burke's view of events. Written in the first person, it gives Burke's account of events from the delivery of the first body to the anatomy rooms of Dr Robert Knox to the hanging of Burke in the Lawnmarket on the 28th January 1829. In contrast to most other books on Burke and Hare, it very nicely combines factually correct information, or what is believed to be factually correct information, in a very readable way. She gets right into the character of Burke and despite the dark subject matter - murder and the selling of bodies for money - she writes with an element of humour.

She also very cleverly links the old with the new and brings the story right up to date. The very first sentence in the very first chapter accurately describes Burke's current residing place and the current condition of the space in which he is on display. The glass paneled ceiling is indeed needing cleaned and the museum roof does leak!

For those wishing to source the material on which this account of Burke and Hare is based, Philp includes notes on every chapter at the back of the book. This is an extremely valuable resource and its comprehensiveness is an indication of the research that has gone into the writing of this book and her meticulous attention to detail.

Of all the accounts of Burke and Hare that have been written, this is one of the easiest to read, giving a factually accurate account of events but presented in a very accessible way. It is altogether a thoroughly enjoyable read.

Gordon Findlater
Professor of Translational Anatomy
University of Edinburgh

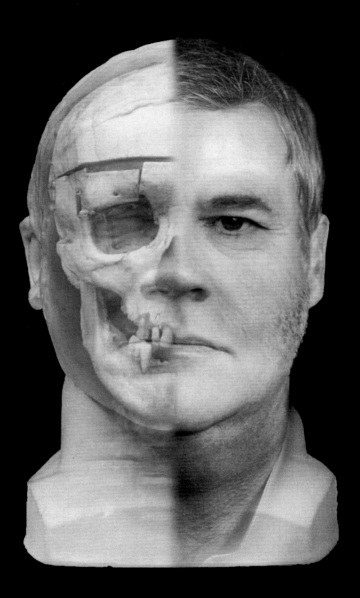

Facial reconstruction of William Burke

Contents

Chapter 1

My Current Prison Cell[1]

The pane of glass had not been cleaned for many years. In a way I wish it were still dirty. Since they tried to clean it I have a big smear that runs across the right hand side of my vision – it distorts my world. They are working their way around the room cleaning up some of the bigger exhibits, the crowd pleasers, the ones that pull in the visitors; my windows were done first. The light coming in from above is disturbed by the dirt on the external panes that missed out on the grand clean up. The morning rays play across the other display cases, highlighting the dust and reflecting on lingering rain drops[2]. It can be a quiet reflective place.

I don't have a problem seeing the people who come and stare at me[3]. They get so close to the glass I sometimes imagine I can feel their breath on my face. They peer at me from every possible angle, they point, they mutter, they judge; I'm sure if the glass were not there they would poke me. I wonder if they would get so close if I was not so restrained. How brave would they feel then?

I'm shut in my prison, an image of my former self only a few feet from my face[4], a constant reminder of the past, my past, the mistakes I made. I have had plenty of time to reflect, to run the scenarios over and over in my head. Where did I go wrong? What should I have done? The answer is simple really – I have a clear view of that now.

It is a clear view of the outside world I miss the most, the humdrum of people coming in and out of the room, the passing conversations, the cups of tea being made, the connection to the normal world that I left so many years ago.

I know I am in this old glass case because of what I did. I was cheated and double-crossed, and yes … guilty

I know I must serve my sentence – for I am William Burke.

(Although I have no idea where the 'e' came from – I always spelt it Burk[5].)

Chapter 2

Disposing of the Dead

In the years I have spent in the museum I often wonder what my life would have been like if I hadn't travelled down the road that I did[1]. Might Nellie[2] and I have made a go of it? My retraining as a cobbler was starting to pay dividends[3]. The streets were so rough and everybody walked everywhere so shoes wore out in a short time; there was always work for a cobbler. Maybe we would have managed to put aside some funds and get larger rooms, maybe have some children[4] – my life could have been so different, although maybe by 35 I was getting a bit too set in my ways. If I had known the path down which I was to travel I might have thought twice about helping out my landlord that November day in 1827.

I was working in my room, rummaging through some of the small bits of leather that Effie[5] had given me a few days earlier, when the door opened and William Hare, my landlord, stumbled in. He had clearly been drinking but that was not unusual – to be fair we both enjoyed a drink. I had met his wife, Margaret, on one of my trips across to Edinburgh a few years earlier[6]. At that point she had been married to Logue but he had died the previous year and she had set herself up with William, one of her young lodgers. It seemed a bit quick after Logue's passing but who was I to judge. Nellie and I bumped into them again just after the Penicuik harvest. We were about to move away to set up my cobbling business down south but Margaret persuaded us to give it one more try in Edinburgh, using a room at their house and the old stable out the back.

He threw himself down on the other chair in the room "Four pounds!" He had been in a mood for a couple of days, since Donald had died. Donald was an old retired army man who had slept in one of the rooms across the hall. He had always kept to himself and survived on his pension which he collected every four months. The Hares must have been allowing him to run up quite a debt as he had died owing them £4 rent. I remember commenting to Nellie that it seemed a bit out of character as they were always on our door the day rent was due, and we were supposedly friends. I think there might have been more of a story to the £4 debt[7] but I was never brave enough to delve into Hare's private business. He was a brash character[8].

When Margaret had discovered that Donald had passed away she was straight onto the authorities to get the parish to pick up the cost of the funeral. I guess if you are already £4 down you don't want to run up any more debt.

"Four pounds! You know what? – I should sell him to the doctors." Hare slumped down into the chair even further. I had seen him talking with a bunch of men last night. Their spades and sacks told me they were up to no good. There was a growing trade in resurrecting people[9] and I assumed this was where he had got the idea about the doctors from. He wasn't known for his innovative thoughts.

"You can't do that – the carpenter is coming this afternoon." I continued to sort through my leather scraps. I had been using the fact that the carpenter was appearing soon as a crutch to get me through the past few days and the growing smell which filled my nostrils at every breath. I was holding onto the fact that the smell would soon be gone. I turned my face and got a lungful of whisky fumes instead as Hare grabbed my shoulder and leaned in close.

"We could do it. I would get the rent that the bugger owes me and if you help me out I'll give you a share....[10]" Someone shouted from the front door but Hare stood his ground beside me, "We could do it William.....we could." He left the room, pointing back at me with a shaky finger.

I assumed the shout was the carpenter and that would be the end to Hare's mad ideas but he returned about half an hour later with a chisel in his hands.

"Come and help me get this lid off." He disappeared along the corridor and I followed after him, keener to see what he was trying to do than to follow through with his stupid idea.

The coffin sat in the middle of the room. By the time I entered, Hare was on his knees applying the chisel to the edge of the boards. His eyes focused down his thin pointy nose giving him a sense of demonic determination that surpassed his usual evil look[11].

"Think about it William – what are you going to do with the body?"

"We'll hide it; fill the coffin up with something." The lid lifted up and, with a crack, sprung off the box. Donald lay in all his inflated glory. He had died of dropsy, parts of his body had swollen up and he had been dead a few days – he had looked better. "Grab his legs, let's get him out." At that point I should have said no but Donald was already dead, he owed the Hares money and it's not as if anyone was going to miss him. He was getting buried by the parish; there was no family. Swallowing my morals for a quick financial gain, I grabbed the legs and we lifted him back onto the bed in the corner, throwing several blankets over him to hide his body. Nothing could hide the smell.

We both stood there, hands on hips, puffing a little and staring down into the empty box. I looked up at Hare, we both looked down at the box. I glanced over at Donald.

"They're going to notice an empty box." It seemed obvious but I wasn't sure Hare had actually thought this through. Rubbing his chin, he murmured his agreement.

"Bark!"

"Bark?"

"Come on," He left the room and raced out into the close. There was a big pile of bark at the back of the tenements. The tannery used it for curing their leather. He grabbed a sack, filled it up and went back inside. I followed suit – it was going to take more than one sack of bark to get anywhere near the weight of Donald. After half an hour we had filled most of the coffin but it was nowhere near the weight of the old army pensioner, it rattled horribly in the coffin, and its distinctive oaky smell was competing with the stench emanating from the blanket covered bed in the corner.

We shoved one of the sheets over the top to try to stop the bark from moving around so much and nailed the lid back down.

Hare stood back, a big grin across his face, evidently very happy with the first, and as it subsequently turned out, only, part of his plan. I looked at the very light, rattling coffin sitting in the middle of that stench filled room and, for what would turn out to not be the last time in my life, I wondered what we had done.

The parish porter appeared maybe an hour later as the two of us were having a drink around the fire in Hare's kitchen area. Conversation had been scarce, what do you say to someone after you have just done what we had done? The porter was McCulloch - I recognised him from around the streets. He would carry anything for anyone, anywhere.

"The cart's at the door. If one of you fine gentlemen would give me a hand, I'll be out of your way."

Hare gave me a nod - he clearly expected me to help hump the coffin out of the house.

We walked into the room and McCulloch's nose gave a bit of a twitch.

"The smell lingers." Hare waved his hand in front of his face and positioned himself between us and the bed which contained the source of the stench. McCulloch said nothing.

As we bent down and lifted up the coffin, I lifted my end quicker than McCulloch. As I did it, there was a scraping noise from inside the coffin as the bark repositioned itself and slid down towards the lower end. McCulloch looked at me, I looked back, and we said nothing. The coffin was carried out of the house, placed on his cart and McCulloch disappeared down the close.

"He must be really stupid…" I started,

"Or, he asks no questions." Hare finished. A quality we would come to rely on in the next few months.

"There is just one problem now." he continued, "How do we sell a body to the doctors?"

A lot of us will have our life affected by a medical student[12]. I see a lot of them every week. Young whelps, wet behind the ears, eager to learn and sometimes too confident in what they think they know. Sometimes they will notice something, or miss something, that will have a life changing effect on someone. My life was certainly changed by a medical student. I see him now as the pivotal point. I could blame him - if he had reacted in a different way I might not be here today, staring out from behind the glass. I might have lived with Nellie in our little house, children at our feet. I might have been happy.

At least I'm almost certain he was a medical student – he might have been a passerby, but whomever it was, that man steered us towards our new roles.

I had no idea how you sold a body to a doctor either. There were men around the West Port who had the reputation of being resurrectionists. They would have known how to get rid of a body but they might not have liked the idea of someone trying to muscle their way in to the action. Not that we were afraid of a fight, we had had our fair share, but there had to be a better way of finding out. Besides, the smell of Donald was throughout the lodging house and we wanted to shift him today.

We headed down to the University buildings on South Bridge and approached someone who looked like they fitted in there – the medical student.

We asked if he knew the whereabouts of the Professor of Anatomy. He seemed amused by this request, - it was late in the afternoon. Apparently back then the anatomy department didn't have the large glass ceiling that I am currently housed under and so the professors disappeared as soon as the light started to fade in the afternoon. He asked us why we wanted to know and, against my better judgment, Hare announced we had a subject for the doctor. This piqued the young man's interest. That's why I have him down as being a medical student. There was a shortage of bodies for the anatomists to work on[13] and I think he saw this as something which would be to his benefit. He directed us to 10 Surgeons' Square, the teaching rooms of Robert Knox.

It was a short walk from South Bridge to the Square and we found number 10 without too much trouble. I cautioned Hare before we knocked on the door. If we were going to be so brazen about having a body for them then at least we should give ourselves false names. I would be John - Hare picked the name of William![14]

The door was opened by a young man who cautiously asked what we wanted. On finding we had a body that the doctor might be interested in, he told us to return after dark. It all seemed a bit too simple.

Although McCulloch hadn't asked any questions about the rattling coffin we didn't want to push our luck by getting a porter to carry old Donald across to Surgeons' Square for us. We had slipped him into an old sack and the corner of it was beginning to dampen with I know not what, nor did I want to ponder on what it might be. It seemed too risky to involve someone else in the venture so that night I hoisted the sack onto my back and the two of us set off. Donald was old and fairly light but, if you'll excuse the pun, he was a dead weight and not an easy carry. About half way there I started to grumble so much that Hare eventually took the load on - I think he would have let me carry it all the way if I hadn't. He didn't have much of a care for other people's welfare, something which would work in my favour, for a while. We got to the square around 10pm.

"Go and knock on the door William." He swung the sack down from his shoulder and stood there panting.

"We can't just turn up at the door with a sack, surely?"

"Maybe you're right." Maybe I was but he wasn't coming up with any other suggestions.

"Let's go and put it by the cellar door, - that will be where they take them in." It was as good a suggestion as I could come up with so we pulled the sack over to the cellar door, brushed down our coats as though it was going to make us more presentable and knocked, for the second time that day, on the front door of 10 Surgeons' Square. The same young man we had met earlier opened the door. He looked at us, looked around us and eventually asked.

"Have you got it then?" We nodded. "Bring it in then." He disappeared from view and much to Hare's annoyance we had to go and get the sack and carry it back to where he had originally dropped it.

Once in the large hall, the young man tapped on the central table. Getting Donald out of the sack was no easier than putting him in but eventually we had his shirt clad body on the table. In my mind I ran through the explanation of how we had come about his body; we had found him in the street; we had purchased him from the poor house; we were doing it as a favour for his family; each one sounded more improbable.

The door at the other end of the hall opened and in walked a smartly dressed figure. I say smartly dressed but I struggle for the proper word. A popinjay? Is that the phrase? A fancy coat the like of which I had never seen - more ruffles and cuffs then I could count[15]. The candle he carried lit up one side of his face giving him a strange one sided appearance[16]. He waved a hand towards Donald and the young man ordered us to get the shirt off the body[17]. The doctor – I assume this was Knox although he hadn't extended us the courtesy of an introduction, prodded the body and murmured and muttered to himself.

"7 pounds 10 shillings. Pay them." And with that he was gone.

The young man handed me the money as we stood on the doorstep.

"If you come across any more we would be happy to see you again."[18] He pushed the money into my hand and shut the door. I stood staring at the wood as Hare reached in and took his share. Had it really been that simple? How many times had I run the story about how we had come about the body through my head and yet no one asked me at all. I felt a little cheated and yet lying in my hand was more money than I could ever hope to get from my cobbling.

"I told you I would see you right William, you keep that and I'll take the debt I'm due plus a little extra." He took my shoulders, turned me around and led me away from the door. "I think we need to celebrate. There is going to be some drinking in West Port tonight!"

Chapter 3

Crossing the Line

Sitting just to my right in the museum case is a sight that always makes me smile. I have limited opportunities for humour now. It is the back of Hare's head, not particularly funny in its own right but the complete lack of hair makes me smile every day.

Back in January 1829, I was in prison waiting to die. Some sculptor came to my cell and took a cast of my head[1], something to do with being able to tell the character of a person from the shape of their head[2]. I obviously knew he had taken the cast of my head but it turns out he had also taken a life mask of Hare. My mask shows a full head of hair. Hare's, on the other hand, is bald[3]. It always gives me a little smile to think of them shaving the bastards' head. I continued to find it amusing even after it dawned on me that the only reason I had kept my hair was that they knew they were going to get my bald head soon enough[4].

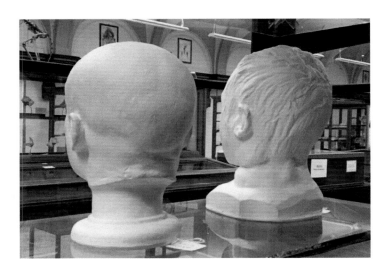

The man I share my current cell with is Howison, John Howison[5]. I don't pick up on his thoughts very often, thank God. They are dark and troubling. He is an evil man. Well, sometimes he is the devil himself, sometimes he seems more like a child, his thoughts wander and vary so much that it is sometimes like sharing the cell with multiple people. I've got a lot of my information about him from the spectators and staff that stop outside our glass cage and talk about us. Mind you, if they are as accurate about him as they are about me then maybe I shouldn't put too much faith in the stories. Grave robber indeed![6]

Howison's thoughts are few and far between. He doesn't seem to reflect on his wrong doings the way some do, the way I do. I can understand that when you know what his wrong doings were! John Howison killed a woman with a spade! A spade! He tried to take her face off with a spade[7]. I don't want to even think about how you die if someone does that to you! At least our victims were all intoxicated with drink when we killed them, most of them seemed unaware of what was happening. We didn't sneak up on people. If you dealt with us then we sat across from you in plain view for several hours, sharing the drinks. To attack someone like he did, someone you didn't even know, it's not like it was over a disagreement or anything, that is just evil.

Evil. That is a strange word and obviously one that has been levelled at me more than once. I wouldn't say that I was evil, well who would describe themselves as evil? I was a man who did evil things. I knew they were wrong. Don't forget that I had had a Catholic upbringing and then worked for a Presbyterian minister[8]; I can give you chapter and verse on what is right and what is wrong. I know it's wrong to kill people. Maybe that is evil, to know it's wrong and to continue to do it anyway. But I would never put myself in the same bracket as Howison. He is not all there. I know he tried to use insanity as a defence[9], and having spent sometime this close to him, I would agree that the man is insane. He scares me. Sometimes his thoughts seem normal, or as normal as you can be as a disembodied museum artefact, sometimes they are so dark that I try to shut them out rather than allow them to start me on a downward spiral of doom and gloom. I have never experienced him reflecting on any of the facts of his case that I hear visitors outside talking about. Maybe that is the issue, he didn't know what he was doing, so maybe he is not truly to blame. I knew exactly what I was doing. I sometimes had to drink myself to obliteration to enable myself to do it but I knew what I was doing, I knew it was wrong and I continued to do it. Maybe I am evil.

I still like to think I was a normal man doing evil things. Evil things? It was a simple business[10]. As a cobbler I made 15 shillings a week, rent was 3d a night. We got £10 for a body[11]. It clearly was not worth working night and day as a cobbler when such large sums of money were so easily available. Do you think that any of the noble gentlemen who turned up in that court house gave any thoughts to those people before we killed them? How many gentlefolk do you think we saw in the streets of West Port? They stayed away, left us to live in squalor, open sewers in the street, tens of people in each room, fighting over scraps of food. People would die in their houses and no one would notice. None of those gentlemen would have raised an eyebrow at all if 16 people had died on the streets by being run over by their horses and carriages. I wonder how many poor people were killed that way during the same year that we were in business. Were they outraged because we were killing people for money, or because they hadn't thought of it first? They didn't care about us at all. Maybe it scared them when we started trading in bodies, after all it's hard to tell a gentleman from a down and out when they are naked on a slab.

The evil thoughts came in February[12]. It had been two months since we had taken old Donald to Knox in exchange for 7 pounds and 10 shillings. I'd like to say that I had set some money aside for my grand plans but I hadn't, it all went on drink. Hare did use some of his money wisely later on. He got a maid for the house and invested in some pigs[13] but for now, the money had run out and with it the whisky.

I came back to the room that cold February day with a few pennies in my pocket from a pair of shoes I had just sold. Nellie had been out selling the other pairs I had fixed earlier in the week so I needed to start work on fixing some of the broken shoes that littered the floor of our room. As I made my way along the corridor to our room I got called on by Hare.

This was not usually a good experience. Hare had more or less given up working when he took over the lodging house. He had a few rooms of seven or eight beds that were for lodgers just looking for a few nights. During harvest season he could have as many as 24 people in each room all paying him 3d a night. His expenses were few and far between, it's not like he spent any funds maintaining the property; the place was pretty run down. If he called on anyone it was usually for money and nine times out of ten he would be drunk. More often than not these visits ended in accusations being thrown around and occasionally a punch or two. He was a very bad fighter so the risk of injury was not great but it always took up time and the chance that you might be chucked out of the boarding house.

"Join us William." He kicked a stool over towards me and lifted up the whisky bottle. I didn't need to be invited twice to drink someone else's whisky.

"What are we drinking to?" As if I cared.

"This is Abigail[14]." He pointed towards an old woman who I had not noticed sitting in the corner, "She's staying the night on her way back to Gilmerton.[15]"

"I'm not staying; I'll be on my way in a moment." She said but didn't make any effort to move. "I've got to get ready for my daughter coming to visit."

"Is this the daughter that I am going to marry?" Hare replied. Clearly a conversation had gone on before I had appeared and Hare was spinning her some line about looking after the daughter. It had obviously slipped his mind that he was married. I refilled my whisky from an already half empty bottle. I suspect another bottle had been finished before my arrival. I had no chance of catching up with these two.

"Aye, that's the one. I must be off." She still made no effort to actually rise from the chair.

"Oh silence woman, there is no way you are going to walk all that way tonight. It's already dark and raining, you'll catch your death if you go out there, assuming you're not robbed before you reach the corner of the street." Hare refilled their two glasses and produced another bottle from the floor beside him. "Am I not right William?"

Map of West Port – Hare's house location shown in red.

"Oh, that you are." I assumed there was some reason Hare wanted this old woman to stay. I guess a nights' rent was better in his pocket than hers. "You'd be better off staying here tonight and make the walk tomorrow. Stay and drink with us tonight."

"Do you sing laddie?" The old woman leaned forward towards me.

"He plays the whistle Abi, voice like an angel as well."

"Go get your whistle lad and I'll sing along." And so we spent the night drinking and singing. Margaret and Nellie came in with some food at some point and joined us. The night became a blur of whisky, food and music, right up until the point when I slumped down on the floor and closed my eyes.

I forced my eyes open and focused my vision. It took a while. The fire place was still smouldering, I could see wisps of smoke drifting off to my left and a foot blocked most of the view from my right eye. I groaned and moved a little. The bed in my room was not great but it was a vast improvement on the floor of the lodgers' room. I pushed myself up to sitting and wiped the back of my hand across my face. Whisky never really gave me much of a head ache the next day; it just obliterated my thoughts at the time. Hare was lying on his back, bottle in hand and Abigail was half hanging out of the bed in the corner. There was no sign of the women. Bracing myself against the wall, I got to my feet and walked a pretty irregular path across the floor to the door and along to my own room.

Nellie was making breakfast. She didn't say anything to begin with just cast me that look that said it all. I lowered myself into the chair and she plonked a plate of eggs down in front of me. I reached for the fork and let my attention wander as the barrage of accusations started to flow.

"Good eggs." The words had left my lips before I realised the implications, obviously I wasn't paying any heed to her scolding. I got a skelp across the back of the head to remind me of my inattention. I had got to my feet and had my arm raised when a squeal from the other room sent her scurrying away.

Hare appeared in the doorway as she left, "The old woman's not well." He explained as he sat down and helped himself to some eggs from our pan.

"Hair of the dog?" I nodded towards the bottle he had brought to the table.

"Maybe, worth a try." He pushed himself up from the table and staggered back down the corridor towards the room.

Two hours later, I was feeling a lot fresher. Nellie had not reappeared after seeing to the old woman, presumably knowing that I would carry on with my retaliation if she came back. She really ought to have known better than to strike me by now[16]. I had sorted out the latest batch of leather bits that Effie had managed to find me from old fire places and street corners and I just needed to collect a few tools from down in the old stable at the back of the house. I made my way along the corridor, past the lodger's room.

"Come and join us William." Hare was back sitting at the fire place, Abigail propped up on an old stool, leaning against the table.

"I should be getting on."

"Nonsense, just one. Hair of the dog was a success. I've never felt fresher." Hare waved the bottle in the air and beckoned me over.

"And how is Abigail?" I straddled the stool and pulled the glass towards me as he filled it up.

"Oh she passed out ages ago. Hasn't made a peep for hours." As Hare said this Abigail roused a little in her sleep, slid off of the edge of the table and collapsed down onto the floor, her legs still caught up in the stool. We looked at each other and snorted in laughter.

It was never just one drink. I could blame Hare but I was never able to have just one even when he wasn't there. It was about lunchtime when he came up with the suggestion that was to change the course of our lives.

Abigail was on the floor still grunting and spluttering away. Being the gentlemen that we were we had not lifted her up onto one of the beds.

"Do you know William, it would not be difficult to take her where we took Donald."

It hung in the air. It was a simple statement of fact and it was right. To this day I am not sure that Abigail Simpson would ever have woken up. I didn't turn to face him but my eyes shot over to him. Was he being serious? He wasn't looking at me but staring into the fireplace. If it had been evening and the fire lit then maybe its strange orange glow would have made him look even more sinister than he did, but in the cold light of day it simply seemed to be a suggestion. Here was a woman who nobody around here knew, she was so drunk it was unlikely she was ever going to wake up again. All we needed to do was make sure and we now knew the route to get an easy £7. Something tugged at my heart.

This was murder.

This was wrong.

I looked over at Abigail, drool running down her face. If she came to she still had to get out to Gilmerton and explain away the fact that she had spent the night in town with two strangers. She hadn't seem too concerned about it last night so I chose to believe she didn't have anyone to explain it to. If her daughter was visiting then clearly she had already moved away and if the offer to be looked after by the likes of Hare was tempting then it must be a pretty desperate situation. She was returning to a cold lonely existence. It was becoming easier to make the decision with every second that I deluded myself.

Hare walked over and pinched her nose; I assumed it was to stop the snoring which had started to invade the silence. Her mouth fell open, a fresh wave of drool spilled down her cheek. He pushed her jaw back into place and then kept his hand there.

"What are you doing?" I jumped to my feet.

"Ah come on William, it'll be the easiest £7 we have ever made." Her leg twitched a little on the floor. "Hold her down." And with that instruction my life changed. I leant across the frail old body and studied her shoes, not wanting to look the other way and witness what Hare was doing. Her shoes were a bit scuffed but they had no big holes, with a bit of work I could get them looking like new and maybe make a few pence on the side. What was I thinking? I smiled at the fact that I was thinking of plans to make a few pence whilst executing a plan that made pounds. Part of me longed for the honesty of the shoe transaction - a few pence for a few hours' honest work - forgetting the fact that they were a dead woman's shoes. Hare didn't actually need me – Abigail didn't stir at all apart from that first initial twitch.

Five minutes later Hare and I were back in our chairs having another

dram. It was almost as though nothing had happened. I could have believed I had dreamed it all if it hadn't been for the evidence hidden under
the straw at the back of the room. We went along to Surgeons' Square
and arranged to meet Paterson, the porter from Knox's rooms, at the back
of the Castle that evening. He carried the box the rest of the way as we
sauntered along behind him, chatting away just as normal.

Knox himself appeared at the rooms, dressed in all his finery. He
stooped down to look into the box and lifted an arm up out of the way
to get a better view. He obviously liked what he saw although it made
my blood run cold. My hands were shoved deep into my pockets to hide
the shaking and the sweat that was pouring off of them; this was guilt. I
would love to be able to tell you that Hare was in a similar quandary but
he looked like a cat in front of the fire.

Knox made mutterings about how fresh the body was and I thought
the game was up. Surely he would ask us how we had come by it, so fresh
and unmarked and yet in a tea chest. He didn't. He nodded to his assistants and they produced the money, £10. Hare took £6, I got £4[17]. I was
happy with this arrangement thinking that the smaller payment in a way
represented the smaller amount of guilt. The cheek of it was that I then
had to pay Margaret Hare £1 out of my share for the use of the house[18].
Still, even £3 was not to be sniffed at and I made sure that Hare got the
first round in - I probably got my £1 back in whisky.

Chapter 4

Angel of Death

Edinburgh had a large Irish population[1]. A lot of them came over at the same time as me in 1818 to try and secure work building the Union Canal. When the general peace had broken out in Ireland all the local militias were disbanded[2] and I found myself back home in Ballina with my wife and children[3]. We were fortunate that her father owned a farm that was still large enough to separate out amongst some of the returning families. We ended up with a small piece of land that was enough to grow the food we needed plus a little bit extra. I wasn't really a farmer but there was no other work which I could do to get money to buy food and so we grew our own supplies. I'd like to be able to tell you what a hard life farming is and how there were times of plenty and then hard winters where we had to eat the same thing every day just to survive, but I didn't hang around that long.

We were lucky that we had access to the land but what I wanted was a lease to ensure that the land would remain ours for a bit longer than from season to season. Her father was not inclined to agree to that. He had some idea in his head that once I got a lease I would sell the land and desert his daughter. The lease was not forthcoming so, not wanting to disappoint him, I deserted his daughter and left for Scotland.

The boats from Ireland to Scotland were crammed with people looking for work with the hope that there was going to be more on offer in a new country. Some of my fellow travellers stayed in Glasgow but most followed the harvest around making as much as they could during that season and scratching out a living buying and selling things during the winter. It was a fairly turbulent time, a lot of very poor people lived in squalor and a few very rich people lived in comfort.

There was a man that boarded at Hare's house who had once been part of those upper classes. Joseph was an old man now but he was tied in, by marriage, to one of the partners of the Carron Iron Company[4], the biggest iron firm in the whole of Scotland. There were nights around the fireplace when he would tell us stories of various parties he had been to back in the day. He never explained how he had fallen to his current social standing; little more than a pauper residing in one of the more respectable houses in Tanner's close.

The entrance to Tanner's Close

It had been a fairly hard winter and I hadn't seen much of Joseph. He spent most of his time in bed underneath as many blankets as possible. On the weeks that I managed to purchase a bottle of whisky I would go and see him.

"Auch Willie, you're awful kind." He would take the glass and knock the whisky back in a single gulp. Usually it put a bit of colour in his cheeks but this week they remained a dull grey. "I don't think I'm long for this world." He let out a rattling cough and convulsed for a few minutes as it racked his body.

"Have you eaten Joe?"

He shook his head and slumped back into the corner of his bed.

"I'll go and see what we've got." I left the bottle in his room, confident that he wasn't going to suddenly come to life and down it all in my absence. As I got to the corridor Hare was standing there.

"Where have you been?"

"Just seeing Joseph."

"Are you mad?" He motioned for me to follow him into his rooms. I was intrigued about the sudden change of heart. He had been relatively compassionate towards Joseph before, well as compassionate as I'd ever seen him towards anyone, even his wife[5].

He shut the door behind us.

"You haven't heard anything then, out on the street?"

"About Joseph?" What could be the word on the street about this frail old man?

"Margaret tells me that people are starting to talk, there are rumours that he's got fever and the house is infected."

"I haven't heard that. It's just rumours; they will have something better to talk about next week." I moved towards the door.

"We've got empty beds and takings are down." Hare walked over to the cabinet and pulled out a bottle of whisky. "Margaret wants me to get him out."

"What! You can't do that, the man is sick. I'll be surprised if he sees next week!"

"Well, he's not going to see it in this house." Hare opened the door and disappeared along the corridor. I was on his heels emploring him to show a little mercy.

When we reached Joseph's room he hadn't moved from the corner where I had left him. Hare gently tapped Joseph's foot with his own and produced a couple of glasses from his own pocket.

"Joseph, tell us again about the good old days." He thrust a filled glass into Joseph's hand, filled his own and settled down beside the bed. It seemed a strange way to evict a lodger. I assumed he was building up some Dutch courage.

We spent the next few hours listening to Joseph's tales of the good old days. They were interspersed with long coughing fits. He had lost a lot of weight since I had last seen him and at places you could see the bones sticking through his thin clothes. He was a sorry sight.

Eventually the whisky took its toll and he passed out on the bed. He lay on the blanket, his face half turned into the small pillow.

"If I ever get that way William, be sure to put me out of my misery." Hare refilled his glass and downed it in one go.

"Aye, he must be suffering."

"We could do us both a favour. We could stop Joseph's suffering and at the same time stop the house from getting a bad reputation."

"How would we.......? No!" I got to my feet as Hare's plan dawned on me.

"Think about it William. He is going to do nothing but suffer until he dies. Each day he lives my rent income goes down and down, and we know we will get an income from the doctor." He sensed my hesitation. "Good God man, he is already face down in a pillow!"

My mind raced. What he was saying was true. Joseph wasn't going to get better from this fever. I had tried to make him as comfortable as possible with the odd shot of whisky but we could help end his suffering altogether. He lived on the memory of the good old days but I had never seen anyone come to visit him. He was alone, suffering and his days were numbered. Was this the final favour I could do the old man?

We rolled him over so that his face was down into the pillow and the two of us leant against him for five, maybe ten, minutes. He didn't move at all. Hare tried to reason it away by saying we had simply hastened things along. If we didn't pack him into a tea chest to take to the doctor that night then we would be doing it before the week was out.

It was just like old Donald although we had helped this one over the edge. At the time it almost made sense.

Obviously it doesn't make sense now to people looking back at the case. Did Joseph know of Hare's plan when we entered the room? He wasn't stupid - what if he had guessed the plan and went along with it anyway? Did that make it less wrong?

I feel a note is maybe needed here about my memory and the order of the murders. You will have to take my word for it, I hope, that when you have committed a large number of killings they all seem to merge together. Remembering individuals becomes a struggle and not something I try to do. I prefer to blank out faces. You'll note that even my two confessions differ in the order people appear. The order of the first two victims was the main point of difference between myself and Mr. Hare with regards to our confessions. Well maybe not the main point; obviously the glaring difference was that he said I was the ringleader in everything whereas I begged to differ. You didn't know that Hare had made a confession? Oh yes, 1st December 1828 in the presence of the sheriff, Mr. Hare made a judicial declaration, same day he turned Kings Evidence. The actual confession was held in the archives of the justiciary office from which it later disappeared. However, I digress; the main difference was the order of these murders[6]. I claimed that Abigail was first whereas he insisted it was Joseph. I was overruled by Sir Walter Scott[7], who, I am sure I do not need to point out, was not present at either event. Why he thinks he can comment on the timeline I do not know. Apparently it is far more likely that Hare was telling the truth as it demonstrates a clear and logical slide into depravity to kill someone who is already sick followed by someone who is not, rather than the other way around.

Oh that the slide into depravity were so logical and not the plunge that I experienced! Even as a condemned spirit I question the reasoning behind it being more logical to kill one person rather than another. Both are illogical and wrong, although I suspect it made Sir Walter Scott more comfortable to reason away our actions than to simply accept that we killed people for money.

I leave the murders in this order because that is the way I remember it. The confession of the only other person present has not stood the test of time and he was a double crossing liar anyway – who are you going to believe?

Chapter 5

Walter Scott

I like Sir Walter Scott's idea that there were logical steps down into the depravity to which we had sunk. It makes it more reasoned and maybe allowed him to explain it away rather than to think that his fellow men could act in such a way out of choice. It was a simple decision for me. We had made easy money with Donald and for us that was just a disposal of rubbish. If we had carried along on that path then we could have made good money there. People were coming in and out of the West Port all the time, a lot of them died in the crammed lodging houses with no relatives around. There was a need to get rid of the bodies. Parish burials were the normal route but there was a business opportunity for a willing individual[1]. Of course that would have required a bit more effort on our part than simply finding someone, getting them drunk and killing them. The choice I had was to continue to work all the hours of the day to make a few pence or to follow the route that Hare and I had stumbled across and make pounds for a few hours' work. The moral block that should have been in the way was already worn down by years of living amongst people who didn't have particularly high standards and its overcoming was lubricated with vast amounts of drink[2].

Once we had killed Abigail and Joseph we were guilty, and there are not different shades of guilt. If I had stopped then I would still be guilty, but I would also be poor. You might as well be hanged for a sheep as for a lamb[3].

Our next victim was an Englishman who was lodging with Hare. I didn't even know his name. He arrived at the beginning of the week having worked his way up the country from Cheshire selling his wares as he went. He hadn't looked in the best health when he arrived and by the middle of the week he wasn't getting out of his bed and had taken on a funny shade of yellow. Given Hare's suggestion last time illness had taken hold in the house I was expecting him to appear in my doorway. He didn't disappoint.

"I think he's gone." He swung around the doorway.

"Oh good, did he get better?" I looked up from the table.

"No, I think he has gone the other way."

"Are you going to send him off to the doctor?"

"I'll pop along to Rymer's and get a chest if you could give me a hand." Rymer's was a local store that sold groceries and had a small back corner devoted to getting the locals drunk, at a price. He disappeared and I was left to my work for maybe 10-15 minutes, he must have stopped for a drink on the way. As predicted he reappeared with a bottle of whisky.

"Quick drink before we start?" He poured out two large measures indicating that this was going to be anything other than a 'quick' drink. Two hours later we stumbled along to the room to pack up the body.

"Take his jacket off William." I reached down to start to remove the jacket and there was a groan. I jumped back.

"He's not dead."

"Aye he is, he hasn't moved for ages."

I pulled at the jacket again and there was another groan.

"No William, he is not dead."

"Is he not?" Hare pushed me out of the way and came up towards the top of the bed. He casually leant over and held the man's nose. There were a few snuffles and then the mouth fell open. "Maybe you're right." He casually pulled the mouth shut with the rest of his hand and nodded me down towards the legs.

"I don't want illness in the house William and I'm sure you could do with a few pounds." I lowered myself down onto the bed and smothered the couple of twitches that came from the legs. I don't know if Hare had already plied him with whisky or whether he was really at death's door but there wasn't much resistance.

There was even less resistance to the £4 that found its way into my pocket.

I'm not quite sure how I justified it to myself or whether I ever did. In the early days no one ever noticed the people that went missing in Hare's lodging house. People came and went; some were regulars but most passed through, staying for one or two nights and then were never seen again. Who would notice if they entered the front door and never left? How many people do you pass on the street every day? Would you notice if one of them wasn't there? Maybe you would if you spoke to the person or at least acknowledged them but most of the people in the West Port kept their heads down. Their habits were irregular so no one was ever suspicious of what was happening in Hare's lodging house. Maybe if someone had asked the odd question about the guests we would have been a bit more cautious but by now we were beginning to have confidence in our new trade.

The only other person we supplied to the doctor[4] where we knew nothing about her at all was an old woman who had come in from the countryside to meet with some friends in town. I didn't have a lot to do with it so the details are a bit sketchy. Hare said that he came home from working at the canal and Margaret had got an old woman in one of the lodger's beds. She had apparently been trying to leave all day but Margaret had plied her with whisky and put her back to bed three times. She was out cold on the bed. Hare claims he just positioned the old woman so that the blankets were in her mouth and went back to work. When he came home she was dead. I got dragged in to help remove clothes and carry the tea chest across to the doctor. That was another £4 in my pocket but I was just the hired help – that one was totally down to the Hare's[5].

Chapter 6

Women

I get a lot of time to reflect on the fairer sex. A lot of them come to see me – maybe more women than men, or maybe I just notice them more[1]. I always had an eye for a pretty face and, even though I say so myself, I was not a bad looking man. Put your disgust at my actions aside for a moment and think about how I managed to get so many people to come along with me for a drink; good looking and a gift for the gab.

Women, of course, lead you astray. I swing between blaming them all for my current predicament and thanking them for keeping me strong throughout.

I went into the army young, barely more than a boy and I was over friendly with Maggie, the first woman there who caught my eye. My Catholic upbringing and time spent with the Presbyterian minister drove me down the path of doing 'the right thing' and I found myself with a wife and children that I never saw[2]. By the time I returned from the army, the one surviving child[3] was grown and my wife was firmly under the control of my father-in-law who refused to give us any land on which to grow crops to sustain us. Do not get me started on my father-in-law, if he had agreed to give us a bit of his land then I would still be in Ireland with Maggie. I left Maggie to come over to Scotland and strangely enough it did pull at my heart. I hadn't seen her in years, but knowing she had chosen to stay there rather than to come with me and set up a new life really cut deep. I wrote pleading letters to her but I never received a reply. I suspect they never got past her father.

I threw myself into the canal work, based up by Polmont. There were women there who worked alongside the men and some provided other services. I don't remember how I met Nellie. She can't be described as a good looking woman. She seldom smiled and the first words from her mouth were often harsh. She had children by some married men and, when the latest ones' wife died, he took Nellie in and they moved away. At that point she was a casual acquaintance[4], easy come, easy go. She wasn't the prettiest, I might have been able to 'do better' as my friends often told me but she came back for me, when her man died, and we moved into a little place in Maddiston.

I stupidly thought this might be the making of me. We settled into village life, turned up regularly at the little church, chatted with neighbours as we walked down the street, the whole works – and then the priest turned up.

He was a weasely little man with more cunning in him than a man of the cloth ought to have. He had recognised Nellie, and done a little asking around and discovered she was still married to the father of some of her children. He had done a bit more digging and discovered my family back in Ballina. He begged me, for the good of my soul, to return to my wife in Ireland and not to continue with this adulterous relationship any longer. If I could smirk when I think back to this now I would. If that poor priest only knew what torture I had in line for my soul he might have begged me a bit harder. He might not have even crossed the threshold if he knew what potential evil lay within. Needless to say he was shown the door and I was excommunicated[5].

I'd like to say I was faithful to Nellie. She was a jealous woman and she often saw competition where there was none. She also missed it when it was there[6]. I am not sure whether I was clever and cunning or whether she chose her fights wisely, I suspect it was mainly the latter.

When we were living in Brown's close we had a wee slip of a girl staying with us. Well, she was more of a young woman actually - a beautiful young woman who shared our bed. Don't judge, that was the way back then – everyone shared the one bed. Nellie got it into her head that something was going on. She took this girl to task about it. I have to say that after years of moving from pillar to post there was something gratifying about two women fighting over me. After some time it was becoming clear that Nellie was actually going to win this fight so I waded in fists flying. I took the young girl away and found her another room to stay in, somewhere a little more discreet than my bed. I was anticipating the police being at my door when I returned[7]. The fight had not been quiet to start with and I was not sure that Nellie was actually going to get up from the state in which I had left her. When I entered the room, I expected a mess to clear up or a blow across my head from behind the door. There was neither, just Nellie sitting on a stool, a kettle on the fire and nothing ever mentioned of it again[8]. I'm not sure if Nellie thought she had won – she had managed to chuck the girl out of the room, it was a kind of a victory. It certainly ran through my mind the only other time I came close to thinking about indulging so close to home. Her name was Janet Brown.

View from Brown's Close 2016

It was April, 1828. By this time in my career it will not surprise you to know that I was haunted by images that swam in front of my eyes whenever I shut them[9]. Sleep eluded me unless induced by a large volume of whisky and even then I kept a candle burning beside my bed so that there was light when I woke. Considering I slept on a straw mattress, it's a wonder I didn't burn the place down. On one Friday morning I had woken with horrible images of faces floating around inside my head.

The whisky bottle had been emptied the night before so I set off to the Canongate in search of some more. I had been sitting chatting to the barman – I think it was at Swan's[10], for about an hour when the two girls stumbled in.

They were striking – maybe more so because they were clearly a little worse for wear at five in the morning than because of their outstanding beauty but they caught my eye and when they ordered a gill of whisky each I gave a little chuckle and thought that they were my kind of girl.

The older of the two looked vaguely familiar but then the women that walked around this area of town all looked very similar[11]. She introduced herself as Janet, her friend was Mary[12]. They had spent the night at Canongate police station; apparently they had been out drinking. They had just moved in together and had been celebrating when they started to be harassed by a group of young men. On seeing the commotion, a passing police officer had offered them a night in the cells for their own protection[13]. It wasn't unheard of and if that was the story that they wanted to tell me then I was prepared to go along with it. We spent the next hour getting cosy by the Swan's fire-place.

By the time an hour had passed I got the impression that Janet was warming to me[14]. The initial coldness had gone, she was smiling more and when money cropped up in the conversation I managed to tell her that I had a sufficiently large income that I would be able to look after her for the rest of her life. I don't know what I thought I was doing. I didn't have a plan, I wasn't thinking of leaving Nellie when I left the house that morning but just being able to spend an hour in the company of a young woman away from all the reminders in my own house was refreshing[15].

When I suggested breakfast they didn't take much cajoling to go along with the plan. Maybe I was looking for a way out, leave town and set up afresh somewhere new. The fact that my income was tied to Edinburgh and my current activities must have slipped my mind. Taking them back to my room was out of the question. My own bed wasn't the place for the sort of activity I had in mind; I had made that mistake before.

My brother, Constantine, lived just off of the Canongate. We were not exactly close but I kept in touch with him now and then. He was a respectable man with a job, a wife and kids[16]. He worked as a scavenger for the police. The room wasn't grand. The fire gave it a bit of life but this morning it was out and the place looked drab. I made a bit of a fuss about the state of the place and Elizabeth, Constantine's wife, got herself sorted and started making the fire. Communal breakfasts like this were not so unusual as to cause comment. Don't get me wrong, I was not in the habit of turning up with strange young women at my brother's house but he was not that fond of Nellie and did not seem overly concerned about my familiarity with my young companions[17].

Elizabeth did us proud. It was a breakfast of substance and I wondered whether she would hear about it from Constantine when he returned from work as she would have used most of their weekly supply. We had tea, bread and butter, eggs and even haddock. As Constantine left, I produced two bottles of whisky I had purchased at Swan's before we left. Mary could not hold her drink, although, to be fair, by this time we had consumed a large amount of it[18]. Janet seemed to think she had been sober for some time prior to this so maybe she was just out of practice. By ten in the morning she was passed out on the table so I lifted her over to the bed, drew the curtains around it and re-joined Janet at the fireside.

Those were some of the most relaxing hours I had ever spent, certainly in the last few months. Warmth from the fire, warmth from the whisky, and warmth from the cheek that lay upon my chest[19]. Of course I had completely failed to mention I was married. Some things are better left unsaid. Eventually hunger drove us out to find some lunch. Mary was still completely passed out on the bed so we left her there and set off into town.

We returned to Constantine's after lunch and returned to our sanctuary beside the fire. The food was starting to counteract the liquor, my senses starting to focus again and that nagging voice in my mind asked me what I was thinking. However food could not return my senses as quickly as the wailing banshee that launched itself across the room. The bed curtains flared out and for a moment I thought Mary had been possessed and had come to take revenge on me. I jumped to my feet to face the terrifying spectacle. Nellie, her face red with rage, her fists up in the air and using language worse than I had heard in all my days on the canal appeared from the bed[20]. Visions of Brown's Close came back to me. Well, here you are again Burk protecting a young woman you shouldn't be dallying with from your wife! This time however the attack was double sided.

"What the....?" Janet was on her feet behind me.

"That'll be his wife." Elizabeth shouted from the door as she quickly disappeared from the scene. The double crossing witch must have been along to see Nellie and told her about the morning activities.

"You're married!"

"Did he not mention that?" Nellie jumped down off of the bed, stepping over Mary, who continued to sleep. I was momentarily angry about that and shot her a glance as if to ask her to credit me with some sense. Of course I hadn't mentioned it! Strangely enough it seemed to inflame the situation. I grabbed the first thing to hand, one of the glasses that we had been drinking from and threw it as hard as I could across the room. It shattered on Nellie's forehead sending glass splinters and splatters of blood across the room. Whilst she was off guard I bundled her up and shoved her out of the door into the corridor, slamming the door behind her and leaning back against it, chest heaving.

"Well, "Janet was rearranging her hair, brushing down her dress, obviously searching for the right words for the situation. "If that's your wife, I can see why you look elsewhere." That made me laugh. I took her waist and pulled her in tight to me.

"I need to see you again." That produced a barrage of abuse from the other side.

"That'll not be hard, we are kind of trapped here." Janet collapsed into my body so we were both now bracing the door.

"I'll get you out."

"Well, if you get me out, I will come back later." The pact was sealed with a kiss. I still dream about that moment as possibly the last human contact I really had. The spark of humanity in me had been flickering for months. That was the moment it flared before it completely extinguished. I took her hand, positioned her behind me and together we sidled down the corridor, Nellie's blows falling onto my head and shoulders, her abusive language washing over us. One final push that sent her reeling down the corridor set us free on to the road outside.

Janet set off towards her accommodation at Leith Street and I set off for a drink.

Several whiskies later I decided I had better return to the scene. Maybe it would be like Brown's Close and Nellie would be sitting at home just waiting for me to return; somehow I didn't think I was going to be so fortunate twice. Before heading home I thought I'd better pop around to Constantine's, see what had become of Janet's friend Mary and give Elizabeth a piece of my mind for interfering in my affairs.

If Janet had been outside waiting I like to think I might have just taken off there and then. I like to think a lot of things about myself that are not true. We could have got out of town, I could have reverted to my original name[21] and we could have just disappeared. It might have taken some explaining; I'm not really who you think I am and we have to move. Do you just casually drop into the conversation that you've committed a few murders and you are fairly sure your partner in crime would be telling the police about you as soon as your back was turned? Hare would have trouble carrying on without me and unless he could persuade Margaret to join him full time he would soon be out of business. He was a vindictive evil man, he would turn on me as soon as look at me. Then of course there was the fact that as soon as I left I wouldn't have anything like the income I had mentioned and I wasn't so stupid as to think the money had had nothing to do with Janet hanging around. Her absence saved me from the dilemma.

When I got inside I had a whole welcoming committee, Hare, his wife and Nellie were sitting there with Elizabeth, having a drink.

"See you've been busy." Hare lifted up his glass and gave a nod towards the bed. I was momentarily stumped. Did Hare think I had been trying to round up more victims? Had Nellie not told him the entire story? Her snort told me otherwise. Maybe he was offering me an out? It seemed a very compassionate thing to do, especially for Hare. He was no fan of Nellie; maybe he was trying to be sympathetic. I looked over to the bed and the still prone figure of Mary. She had been out cold for several hours – she might already be dead for all I knew. What to do? – call his bluff and say I was doing nothing of the sort, leaving the only explanation to be of an adulterous nature, and in front of my wife. His smirk told me he knew what was going through my mind.

"She dead?" I asked, avoiding the unasked question about my activities that afternoon.

"Don't know." Hare put down his glass and walked over to the bed. We both stared down at Mary. He lifted up the head. "Might be." We rolled her over. There was a flurry of activity behind us as the women disappeared from the room. "Better make sure." He pinched her nose with one hand and placed the other under her chin. I laid down on the bed across her body to stop her wriggling around but there wasn't any movement at all – I think she was either already gone or was well on the way.

"We'll go and get Paterson." Hare pulled the blanket out from under the body and threw it over the top, "He'll have a box."

The very short walk to Surgeons' Square took us a few hours as we stopped for several refreshments on the way. I didn't feel inclined to share my thoughts with him and he only seemed to be fishing for the juicy details. By the third or fourth drink we were drinking in silence. Paterson provided us with a crate but he was too busy to come back and help us move the load. Elizabeth took great delight in informing us upon our return that Janet had been back looking for Mary.

"She came back, looking for her friend." What she meant was that she hadn't come back looking for me. I was resigned by now to the fact that I wasn't going to walk away from this situation. It was too complicated. If I wanted to find an out then I would have to create it myself not look for someone to extricate me from it.

"Should we wait until she comes back again?" Hare posed the question as we took the clothes off the body and lowered it into the box.

"I don't think so. She has spent the day drinking with me and she is nowhere near drunk. I think she could drink us both under the table. There will be easier ones." And with those words I saved Janet Brown from the same fate as her friend. She never got to appear at my trial – a legal issue I will elaborate on later, but her testimony was published. Remembering parts of that afternoon gets me through some of the tougher times.

However, I did get to repay Elizabeth for the kindness of running off and summoning my wife that afternoon by enlisting my brother, her husband, to help us carry the box back to Surgeons' Square[22]. There is nothing like a bit of fraternal implication. No sooner had the box touched the ground than he ran away, taunted by the children who had followed us along the streets. He would later claim he had no idea of what was inside the box but he wasn't that stupid.

Knox's assistants were as pleased as always to see us. They helped us unload the box and lay the body on the table.

"Where did you get this body?" The tallest of the three seemed to recognise the girl and for a moment I thought we might have over stepped the mark[23].

"We purchased the body from an old woman at the back of the Castle, died in her lodging house." It was a fairly reasonable explanation although the girl looked no nearer death than you or me, - well you anyway.

The tall man, Fergusson, looked at her from this way and that. One of his colleagues reminded him that the girls in that area of town all looked like peas in a pod anyway. His remark had some truth although this girl didn't look like any of the girls I had seen in 'that area of town'. I'm not one with an eye for beauty, well look at my wife, but even as she lay on the dissecting table she had a striking appearance that hadn't been quite so apparent when she was unconscious at my table, whisky bottle in her hand.

I was handed scissors to cut off her hair, I assume they sent it to wig makers. We would have to remember that one in future to increase our earnings. At that point we left.

I've heard since that Knox actually got a local artist[24] in to paint that body and he kept it for months in spirits because he was so impressed with it. Maybe we should have charged him more.

Chapter 7

Inappropriate Behaviour

What crosses the line? What is sick, inappropriate behaviour?

Executing someone who has killed others is probably an acceptable punishment, and I think I am in a better position than most to voice an opinion on that. When I started in my line of work I knew that execution was a possible outcome and I chose to take that risk because the rewards were worth it. Hanging in 1829 meant strangulation[1]. I understand that there is now a more humane version whereby they break the neck and the person dies instantly. That would have been better and I would have preferred to go that way, but strangulation didn't seem unjustified considering what I had done. In a way it was very appropriate. What is it the good book says? - do unto others....

I knew that, in line with the 1751 Murder Act, I would be delivered to the anatomy department and anatomised and, ironically, that was justified as well. I had made my living by delivering others up to that very fate so I should suffer it too. It didn't make a lot of difference to me what happened to my body after death. I didn't subscribe to the belief that the body had to be whole to have any thought of getting to heaven and to be honest I hadn't pinned too many hopes on my getting to heaven anyway. No, I didn't dwell too much on what they would do with the body, and, having seen it, I am not going to regale you with it.

Taking bits of skin and preserving them to make wallets; that would be bordering on the sick in my opinion[2]. Dipping your pen in my blood and writing with it; sick[3]. What does it achieve? If they had wanted to put people off following my example then I think my skeleton serves that purpose[4]. Having bits of me preserved and kept as treasured items, that just seems wrong. I know I was a fairly stocky person but I suspect that if you take all the bits of me that have been preserved I would be the size of an elephant!

Of all the murders that I was involved with there is one that weighs on my mind more than most and at the time it led me to drink even more. When I was sober and shut my eyes the face of that particular victim came before me and I felt sick to the pit of my stomach. I tried to blank it from my memory with drink and other means[5], and then, when I was drunk, the crimes and abuse became easier.

So, what was so different about this victim? His age and innocence. What grieves me even more about this particular victim is the wild stories that developed after my arrest. Lies, the only purpose of which was to demonise me even more. I needed no assistance in that department - after all, I had murdered 16 people!

It was around midsummer, we were eight months into our new line of business. With the amount I was drinking it was difficult to keep track of exactly what we did and when. I know that sounds awfully callous but I never kept track of time in the way that people seem to now a days, and these were events I was trying to forget anyway.

I had come across an old beggar man in one of the doorways of the West Port. He didn't take much persuading to follow me home for a dram. We were just walking past Rymer's when I heard an Irish lilt behind me.

I looked around and found an old woman, well, older than me, with a young child, maybe 12 years old, in tow. Putting on my broadest Irish accent I asked her how she found herself in these parts[6].

Turns out she was in town looking for charity to keep her and her grandson from starving. She was old and frail, and looked only a few weeks away from starvation. She was more than delighted to be asked home by a fellow Irishman. The old beggar man could wait for another day.

We were only a few minutes from the house and I expected that Hare would be there as he didn't leave the house much, spending most of his time around the rooms, drinking.

Margaret Hare invited the woman to pull up a chair as we entered the room- luckily she didn't ask me her name as I hadn't bothered to find it out. The woman was very happy to join us around the fireplace, take a glass of whisky and a crust of bread. The boy sat down on the floor beside the fire. There was some discussion as to the whereabouts of his mother and a moan about the current generation not taking its' responsibilities seriously. The boy was mute and deaf and had been handed over to the grandmother to care for. Hare filled up everybody's glasses and gave me a knowing wink.

"Good work William. I think we could run to a second bottle." He flicked a glance at Margaret, indicating that she should go and get some more supplies from Rymer's.

"I'll go." As I pushed myself up from the table the old woman looked up, maybe a little nervous that I was leaving her with people she had known for ten minutes less than she had known me.

"I'm just popping out for some more supplies." I pointed at the bottle.

"Send your woman." Hare protested. Now, I'm not going to pretend that I was a great pioneer of women's rights. Women had their place - a lot lower down the pecking order than me. I lived with Nellie because she provided me with a few comforts, food on the table, companionship and she was there for the more basic urges; but if it hadn't been her it would have been someone else. When she stepped out of line I let her know about it, often in a very physical manner[7]. The same went for Margaret. I wasn't offering to go out to save them the trouble - I wanted to get out of the house.

Although we were pulled up to the fire in the house, it wasn't that cold out. It was June[8] after all. I trudged along the street to Rymer's.

"Ahh William, what are you doing?" The voice in my head asked me. "About to murder another poor wretch?" But she was alone, a stranger here, no one was going to miss her, and I would be £3 better off.

There was no point stopping now. I would simply go back to being poor and having to scrape a living together. Hare and I had a growing reputation as resurrection men. I had promised Nellie that this was not the case; we were simply buying bodies from other boarding houses and selling them on. She seemed to accept that. It explained the money that appeared every so often. By this time we had already killed 5 or 6 people. In my mind I was already living on borrowed time. I might as well be well off whilst I waited to be caught.

I returned from Rymer's knowing what I would do that evening.

The old woman, I never did know her name, was already very merry by the time I got back. Hare took the bottle and topped up everyone's glass. I let him fill mine to the brim. We had established a method of killing people whilst being fairly drunk ourselves, it made it easier.

We chatted about Ireland and the good old days. They can't have been that good as we had all chosen to leave, but things were always better looking back. It was getting dark by the time Hare suggested that the old woman might want to go through and have a little sleep in the bed.

"Aye, I'll maybe just have a lie down." She started to get up but stumbled. Hare and I helped her to her feet. She made some signs to the child who was amusing himself by the fire.

"He'll be fine with the women." Hare reassured her and we led her out of the room, almost dragging her across the old floorboards.

Once in the back room and on the bed her fate was sealed. Actually her fate was sealed the moment she met me on the street but it seemed like the final hurdle as we sat down in the room and watched her drift off into a whisky fuelled sleep. We finished her off in the same way we had dealt with the others. Hare and I were still sitting in the room when Margaret came through the door. We should have locked it.

"I think he wants to know where she is." She quickly glanced at the bed.

"Tell him she is sleeping." Hare motioned towards the bed. She took another glance. At court, Margaret would deny knowing anything about it but she clearly knew then that the old woman was not sleeping[9].

"What are we going to do with the boy?"

"We could take him for a walk in town and just lose him. He would never find his way back here. It's not as though he can tell anyone what happened." Hare wasn't exactly gifted in the intelligence department.

We took the whisky bottle through with us to the front room again, leaving the door open so that the 'sleeping' body was visible to all.

The boy was obviously concerned about his grandmother; he popped along the corridor to look into the room – we didn't stop him. He came back a little more content and settled down by the fire. We gave him a dram to settle him further[10].

I don't want to go in to the details of what happened next as it really does lie heavy on my heart. Needless to say we finished the boy off in the same way as we had all the others. I will never forget the look in his eyes, the pleading stare made worse by the fact that he couldn't voice his fears. Those eyes are forever burnt into my mind. There was no big struggle; he was a fairly feeble lad who had had a fair amount to drink but....that was wrong.

We laid him on the bed beside his grandmother and went to our own slumber. I drank most of the rest of the bottle before I laid to rest.

The next day we wedged the two of them into a large herring barrel and heaved it up on to the back of Hare's old cart. The plan had been to use his horse to pull it along to Surgeons' Square and trade it in. It went as planned until we reached the meal market. At that point the horse simply stopped and refused to take a step further.

It was an old horse and it was left to fend for itself in the stable. Often, when I was in there fixing shoes, I'd give the beast a pat and a few kind words. The large brown eyes were always a bit wary as if waiting for punishment. Hare had purchased it a few years before for a very small amount of money.

Hare started to rant and rave. He approached the horse from behind and smacked its hind quarters. If it had only had the energy, it should have kicked him but it looked as though it was about to keel over. He was making such a scene that people started to gather around us.

"Stupid bloody animal." He smacked it across the rump again, "Move!"

"Let's just move it with a barrow" I shouted over to him and, with a quick nod of my head, indicated the growing crowd.

"Aye." He kicked the horse and admitted defeat.

One of the local barrow boys was passing by so I grabbed him, came to a quick arrangement about the price and we jumped up onto the cart to remove the barrel. He helped me drag it to the back of the cart and then he jumped down and took the barrel and lowered it onto his cart. He didn't ask what was in the barrel although clearly it wasn't herring.

"You guide him, I'll go ahead." I left Hare with the barrow boy and set off at a brisk pace down the street, pausing only to give the old horse a quick pat.

The walk to Surgeons' Square wasn't long although it took longer to cover the distance during the day than it did at night when the streets were empty. Why were we moving the barrel during the day? I don't know. Working at night seemed to be an inconvenience that we didn't need to trouble ourselves with. No one had ever challenged us as to what we were moving around the town so why do it under cover of darkness? I moved through the crowds easier than the two following me with the barrel. I saw a few people I knew, there were a few nods of acknowledgment but, what I saw most often were the searching eyes of the child from the night before. Each face that turned towards me seemed to possess those same pleading eyes. Even the horse seemed to be pleading with me not to carry on down this path. Maybe it had refused to move because it knew what it was carrying. Maybe even the animal kingdom was sitting in judgement on us.

We got to Surgeons' Square without any issues. The barrel was offloaded at No.10. We paid the barrow boy a few pennies and received £16 ourselves.

The horse was rewarded with a bullet. Hare was not a forgiving man.

This was undoubtedly the point at which my drinking became more intense. I had been a drinker before we started down this route, please don't think that I was an angel in my previous life. Once we started supplying the doctor I spent more time drunk than sober. After we had killed the young boy I rarely knew sobriety, I drank hard. I was frequently woken by nightmares, I was plagued by images of his eyes; the pleading dark pools of innocence. Some authors have the audacity to claim that I killed this child by breaking his back[11]. Have you ever tried to break someone's back? Stupid question. You are less likely than me to have tried it. We placed bodies in some very strange positions trying to force them into tea chests and barrels – never once did we manage to break a back[12]. Why would we try and break the back of a child when we had a tried and tested method that worked well? Why these authors feel the need to demonise me even more than I have done myself is beyond me. I know I am not in a position to complain about people kicking a man when he is down but that is unnecessary character assassination. Just stop for a minute and think where medical science would be if we hadn't come along[13].

Chapter 8

Highs and Lows

The Scottish judicial system is one of the best in the world. Fifteen of your peers, all good men, decide your fate[1]. Torture isn't meant to appear in the judicial system at all. From sentencing on Christmas Day 1828 (not the best Christmas present I ever got!) to the point that I was killed on the 28th of January 1829, I was meant to be fed on bread and water and allowed that time to ' humble myself in the sight of Almighty God'[2]. Let me tell you now, it does not take a month to humble yourself in front of God. I knew I was guilty when we were arrested on that first day in November. By the time of my trial, I had already had two months to prepare myself for the inevitable- I didn't need another month. That is torture! Why did they keep me alive for another whole month? It specifically says in the Murder Act that the condemned will be killed within three days of sentence being passed unless that third day is a Sunday, unless of course he is in Scotland, in which case it will be a time period of not less than thirty days, and if you are north of the Forth, forty days[3]. They spent those 30 days well. There was a plan to prosecute Hare. I had a few visits to my cell from the lawyer of the Wilson family. Would I be prepared to give evidence in the case against William Hare for the death of James Wilson? Would I! They didn't have to ask me twice as to whether I would stand up in court and tell them exactly what Hare had been up to. I had nothing to lose from telling them everything. I would get some sort of satisfaction from appearing there and looking down on his face the same way as he had looked down on me that day in court. The only difference would be that I would tell the truth rather than the web of lies that William Hare spouted. It never came to anything. I hear that it got scrapped. The Wilsons had no money to pay for lawyers and Hare had no money to his name. With it being a civil case it would have been for money rather than his life[4]. He had protected that by turning King's Evidence[5]. It would have been nice if there had been a verdict connecting him to the murders. I would have liked to have seen that.

There are some things I have seen that I would not ever want to see again, and then there are some things upon which I could gaze for ever, fortunately. I have had some breath-taking views, I've also spent a lot of my time looking at the inside of a barrel[6] but, on the whole, the former has outweighed the latter.

One of my first homes was in the newly opened three storey anatomy museum in Teviot Place[7]. It was a sight to behold[8]. All sorts of exotic relics from foreign shores and me, ironically, one of their most prized possessions.

The view used to be filled with various skeletons. I used to be able to see a large skull, I have no idea what it was from, it was maybe three foot long with massive long teeth from both its top and bottom jaw. It sat, unmoving, at the feet of what was clearly an elephant. There used to be two elephants standing side by side like two guards. I couldn't see what

was at the feet of the other elephant. I thought we had lost them when they disappeared from the museum but I was briefly reunited with them for a while a few decades ago and then more recently when I featured in a film! That's right - I'm a film star now[9], although not paid what's due – some things never change! I've heard the story bore very little resemblance to what actually happened but at least I got a mention and a cameo appearance.

The elephants are downstairs now guarding a doorway. Maybe it was too much work to get the elephants up to join us again. Even if they were here they couldn't bring the museum back to its former glory. It used to be crammed with so many items that you didn't know where to look. Above the elephants there were skeletons so large that it was hard to believe that such an animal ever existed. They were hung from the ceiling with large cables, taking up most of the length of the room. Whales, they were. I never saw one in my life but my education has continued after my death. When you hang around for hundreds of years listening to conversations, you pick things up. In front of the elephants were three busts of the great and the good - or not so good in my view, as they were all anatomists. Centre stage was Alexander Monro. Not the Monro who played his part in my fate but his father, the eminent Munro secundus. He was flanked by John Goodsir and William Hunter, both after my time on earth and therefore beneficiaries of the changes to anatomy teaching that I brought about.

Behind them was squeezed in a statue I tried my best not to let my eyes rest on. It was a reclining figure, draped over a black marble base as though resting. It wasn't until you studied it closer that you noticed the skin was missing and all the internal organs were on display. It was a masterpiece of sculpture but was a bit too close to my own demise for my liking[10].

I spent a few years packed away in a box to re-emerge into what initially looked like a different room. The busts had gone, the elephants that were behind them had disappeared[11], the flayed man had fled. It was some time before I realised that I was actually still in the museum but on what used to be the third floor balcony and that the big hall had gone - a cheap floor in its place. I used to look out onto the contents of the museum and could watch the people walking around enjoying all the displays. I lurked in the shadows behind them, unnoticed unless they happened to turn around. Now I stand facing the door. I can see them come in by spying through the other glass cases between me and the door. I get to judge them before they make a beeline to my case to judge me.

Judging on appearances is something that we are all told not to do and yet more often than not it is quite a good guide. Clearly the police of Edinburgh were not very skilled at it back in 1828.

Andrew Williamson was one of the local policemen who often frequented the West Port[12]. Usually the police route was a very quick walk down the main street, keeping well clear of all of the closes - enough to say you had been in the West Port but not enough to actually notice anything that was happening there, thankfully.

On this particular day I came across Williamson with another man that I recognised, arm in arm with an old woman who was clearly the worse for wear.

"She's not your usual sort." I joked as I approached them. It surprises many to find I was on talking terms with the local police force. Andrew dropped her to the floor and stood up to chat.

"Ahh, William. We've spent the last 30 minutes trying to drag her along to the watch house. Maggie was complaining that she was outside her shop and it was driving away trade."

"Aye, cause Maggie's shop is always so busy." We had a little laugh at the expense of the competition to Rymer's grocery and bar.

I bent down to look into the woman's haggard face. She was maybe sixty, missing most of her teeth and had a glazed expression that I suspect was not all down to the amount of drink she had had. The smell of money wafted under my nose.

"Why are you taking her to the watch house, she lives the other way." I jerked towards my rooms with my thumb.

"You know her?" Andrew seemed positively delighted. Dare I chance my luck and take someone directly from the police?

"Yeah, she lives just around the corner from me. Do you want me to take her home?" I dared.

"Mmm."

"Andrew, she's an old woman down on her luck, you don't need to be filling up the watch house with this sort." I reached down and grabbed one of her wrists, hauling her up onto the side of my body. I'm not a tall man[13], but I was taller than her. Her shoes brushed along the ground.

"Make sure she gets home safe then." Andrew brushed his hands down his trousers and the two men walked off in the opposite direction.

"Where did you find her?" Hare said as I lowered the woman down onto the bed and stepped back to look at the bounty. Hare peered into her face.

"You are not going to believe this. Andrew Williamson gave her to me."

"Andrew Williamson the policeman?" Hare took a step back as though the police presence had somehow contaminated the body. I relayed the whole story to Hare, he seemed satisfied that we had simply taken a problem off of Andrew's hands, and even more pleased that it appeared we were not going to have to waste any whisky over this one. The woman hadn't stirred since she had entered the house. We spent the next 30 minutes downing a bottle of whisky and discussing the inadequacies of the police force. It was bad enough that they didn't realise that there was a household full of murderers in the West Port[14], but to start handing victims over to them seemed to be a wanton disregard for their duties. Eventually it was getting to the point where the women would be coming home and we could put it off no longer. I'm not sure the woman would actually ever have woken up of her own accord even if we hadn't given her a helping hand. I applied my weight and Hare applied his hand to her face. There was barely a twitch as she passed over.

Another hour's work with the tea chest and a porter and we were £10 richer.

By this time we had killed a lot of people and no one had ever come around asking any questions about their disappearance[15]. No one seemed to care. We were careful to pick people who were from out of town; travelling visitors. We used to ask them questions about themselves as we got them drunk. Any mention of there being someone waiting for them to return and we thought twice. It was too easy. We began to think we were invincible – no one was ever going to catch us - we could kill anyone we liked and get away with it. It's clear, looking back, to see that this was our downfall. We drifted far away from our winning formula with our last three murders but the greatest deviation happened that summer with Effie.

Effie was a beggar. She used to make ends meet by raking through people's fires and collecting up the scraps that were not completely burnt. I'm sure she got some of her food that way too as there always seemed to be black smudges around her mouth. When I first arrived in town and set up the cobbling business she had appeared with some scraps of leather that I used to patch the inside of a few boots. She was a fairly regular supplier of bits and bobs. She always had a big smile on her face - usually a dram inside her from somewhere. She had appeared at the stable door that day with a handful of scraps. I could use them to patch a few little holes but they weren't great. I gave her a few pence and a nod towards the bottle of whisky that was standing on the corner of my workbench. She settled herself down into the straw in the corner and took a few swigs. I returned to my work as she chatted on. I didn't notice that she had gone quiet until Hare appeared at the doorway.

"Are you entertaining women out here now William?" He sneered. I hadn't been entertaining women anywhere for a few months at this stage; an old injury was causing me some pain and discomfort[16]. It wasn't the sort of thing I discussed with people, especially Hare. I looked over to the straw and saw that Effie had collapsed back into the bale, whisky bottle still in her hand. I smiled - it was good to see someone enjoying themselves. I looked towards Hare and saw him grinning like a Cheshire cat. He nodded his head towards Effie.

"It's Effie!" I protested.

"It's £10 waiting to be taken." He walked over to the straw and clamped his hand onto her face. There was a little flurry of straw as her hands tried to grab at something. I walked over and pinned her down. If he was going to kill her I might as well get my share of the money.

It was the first person we killed that we had known for more than a few hours.

That was our first mistake.

Chapter 9

Bannockburn

Each year the people in the village of Maddiston head up towards Stirling and celebrate the anniversary of the Battle of Bannockburn[1]. Any excuse for a party. This would be the tenth year that Nellie and I had attended the event. We barely knew each other the first time we attended; well we barely knew each other at the start of the day, - we were rather more familiar by sundown!

We had made a point of trying to get back to the event each year. It was a good time to get together – you heard about any work which might be available and caught up with old friends.

There was a large Irish population who had never strayed too far from Polmont after the canal work so it was a chance to meet up with old friends and familiar faces, relax, have a drink and generally forget what else was going on. This year, I had more to forget than most.

I particularly wanted to forget the meeting with the Hares just before I left.

I had been in the stable out at the back of the house. I'd just finished off another pair of shoes and Nellie had packed them up in her bag and headed off into the streets to find a buyer. Margaret Hare appeared within seconds of Nellie leaving. I suspect she had been watching us from the doorway.

"Do you think she'll find a buyer William?"

I shrugged in reply.

"She seems to find more buyers than you fix shoes."

I looked up with what I hoped was a face that told her to stop going down this route. Was she suggesting that my wife was selling something other than shoes?

"Just what I heard." She said and took a few steps into the stable fiddling with a few bits of leather that were lying around. "You can't really trust these Scots." She paced around in the doorway.

"Were you after something, or did you just come down here to annoy me?" I had never had much time for Margaret Hare. She was the original connection between myself and Hare as I had stayed at her lodging house in the past, although I had always had more time for her first husband. She was a mean, snobby woman.

"William has gone along to Rymer's and wants you to join him. I'll walk along with you." She attached herself to my arm like a bad smell and led me along the road. I noticed her fancy shawl had been replaced by the standard black one. Money must have been getting a bit short. The finery that she treated herself to seemed to go in and out of the pawn shop with regularity.

Rymer's had a few old wooden chairs tucked into a back corner where William Noble, the shop boy, made a few regulars comfortable with smaller than required measures of whisky.

Hare was ensconced in our favourite back corner nursing a very small drink. Noble made to come over as we went to the seats. I waved him off, I didn't feel inclined to subsidise the Hares' drinking.

"Nellie out selling shoes?" Hare asked.

"Yes and she is just selling shoes before you go down the same path as your trout of a wife."

Hare shot an accusatory glance at Margaret but did not jump to her defence.

"She's just jealous. Do you not think if I could make money putting my wife on the street I would have done it by now?" He sneered at his attempt at humour,

"Seriously though, she is not on the same level as you and me, are you sure we can trust her with our business?" He gave in and waved Noble over. I got my first free whisky of the day.

"She doesn't know anything about our business[2]. As far as she is concerned we buy bodies from boarding houses and sell them on."

"How does she explain the money then?" Margaret Hare chimed in.

"How do you?"

"I run a respectable lodging house." She seemed somewhat affronted by the question and pulled herself up to her full, very short, height. "I can always explain money."

"She's told people she has a legacy from a relative of her late husband up in Stirling, or….and you'll like this one Margaret." I gave her a cheeky nod and a wink, "She has told people that I am a favourite of a lady in the New Town and she will never see me short of a few pounds.[3]" Hare snorted into his whisky and Margaret glared at me.

"Anyway," Hare continued, "I'm not sure we can trust her. You could do a lot better. Why don't we make her disappear and get you a good Irish lass."

"Make her disappear?" I queried. I was fairly sure I knew what he was suggesting but I just wanted to be clear about it.

"Trade her in for £10. You are just about to go off to Falkirk. Write and tell us she got ill and died, come back in a few days' time and no one will be any the wiser."

"Are you serious?" I don't know which I was more surprised about; the fact that Hare was suggesting I kill Nellie or the fact that he was talking about 'trading people in' so openly in public. My blood began to boil and I could feel my face turning red with rage. I'm usually very mild mannered. Margaret tried to make soothing noises and reached out to cover my hand on the table. I pulled it back and instinctively gave her a back handed swipe across the face. Mild mannered might have been over playing it a bit.

"Ah come on William." Hare leaned in closer although he made no attempt to defend his wife who was sprawled on the floor. "We both know that if we run out of victims we would use the two we have on hand all the time."

"You might." I stood up, downed what was left of my whisky and, stepping over the body of Margaret Hare, I left the shop.

"Think about it." He shouted after me.

Nellie and I went to Falkirk the next day having not seen the Hares again.

I had no intention of killing Nellie. She was maybe the one thing that kept me semi grounded in all of this. She had no idea of what we were up to. Well, she might have put two and two together but I certainly never made her any the wiser. When she asked about it I simply told her we were buying bodies from lodging houses and passing them on to the doctors. It wasn't a very savoury trade but it was completely legal and, apart from asking me to confirm that we were not resurrecting people, Nellie seemed content with the explanation. It is to my absolute shame that she had to be tried with me and my absolute relief that she did not suffer the same fate. Of the four of us she was the most innocent and I went out of my way to ensure that that was the case. She suffered enough at my hands with the beatings and infidelity[4] but to murder the woman would have been going too far, even for me.

Bannockburn was good and although my Scottish history is not great, I spent a few lazy afternoons condemning the English and drinking far more whisky than was good for me.

We arrived back to find the Hares in good form. The house had been tided, a stew of sorts was on the boil and a full bottle of whisky sat on the table. They invited us in and sat whilst Nellie told them all about the festivities. At first I thought they were embarrassed about our disagreement before I left. They certainly seemed to want to be friendly again. Then I thought they were maybe going to go ahead with the plan and were just trying to ply Nellie and me with enough whisky. I had spent four days drinking harder than normal and even in my normal state I could drink Hare under the table so I was prepared to sit back and let him try. As the evening rolled on Margaret got sent out to buy more supplies. As she swung the polka dot shawl around her shoulders everything fell into place.

The shawl was back from the pawn shop. The standard black shawl relegated to the cupboard again. There was only one way that Hare had got that much money in a few days. He had been doing business without me!

With Margaret gone and a noticeable tension in the air, Nellie excused herself.

"Business been good?" I asked, hoping it sounded like a casual question.

"Well, it will pick up with harvest in a few months." Hare lifted his legs up onto the vacant seat.

"That's not what I meant." I tried to fix him with a stare but he was looking everywhere but at me.

"I don't know what you mean."

"The shawl is out of hock, where did you get money like that? You've been working without me."

"I've done no such thing." Hare jumped up to defend himself but still didn't meet my gaze. "We've had a lot of lodgers."

"At 3 pence a night you've had a hell of a lot of lodgers!"

"On my honour, William." This time he looked me straight in the eye, "I have not been working without you."

"On your honour?" Honour meant something in Ireland and in the Militia.

"On my honour." We sat back down. I wasn't convinced. Maybe Margaret had taken to selling herself on the street to prove him wrong, maybe they had had a lot of lodgers. It still didn't feel right. I comforted myself for the rest of the night by drinking his whisky – a lot of it.

The following day I found myself down by Surgeons' Square. It hadn't been my intention to end up there but something drove me towards it and at lunchtime I saw Paterson, Knox's man, head off towards a bar.

I followed him in and we chatted for a while whilst we ordered drinks. He didn't want to be seen sitting down with the likes of me but he seemed pleasant enough as we stood there waiting to be served. Apparently if I had any other subjects like the one delivered last week then he would be happy to arrange for transportation. It seemed inappropriate for us to be getting our womenfolk to help out. I told him I would bear it in mind and then I left. I spent the next few hours walking around the streets to calm down. I bumped into Nellie and, by the time I returned to Tanner's Close, we had our plan worked out.

I was packing up my cobbling bits and bobs when Hare made his way into the room. Nellie and I hadn't had much to our name since we lost all of our possessions in the fire that burned down Mickey Culzean's first boarding house in Portsburgh where we used to live[5]. We moved with Mickey to his next venture in Brown's close for a time before we headed off to Peebles but we had never really got back into the habit of having any possessions. I guess once you had lost everything it seemed a bit futile to gather things up again only to run the risk of losing them again. Anyway, it made moving easier.

"What are you doing?"

"We are moving out." I nodded towards the money on the table. "That's the weeks' rent."

"Where are you going?"

"We are going along to Broggan's. He is looking for someone for his room." John Broggan had a room just along the road by Grindley Street. His wife was some sort of distant relative of mine and we had known they were looking for lodgers for some time. John Broggan was burnt as a child and it had affected his appearance so that some people found it disturbing and didn't relish the idea of living with him[6]. It was a small room surrounded by neighbours, but off of its own passage where I could get on with business without any interruptions[7]. At that time I was genuinely thinking of breaking away from this lifestyle. "At least I know I can trust him."

"You can trust me William, have we not been through a lot together?"

I looked across as him. I couldn't begin to put into words what I was thinking. I tried to sum it up in one sentence.

"I saw Paterson. He told me you were there last week."

"Ahh, William." Hare seemed to visibly shrink a few inches. "I wanted to tell you."

"You denied it to my face, you lying bastard."

"The opportunity just presented itself. She was an old woman, much too much to drink…."

"I don't care. You lied to me; on your honour…you lied to me." I put the last thing into the top of the box, lifted it up and walked out hoping never to see William Hare again[8].

Chapter 10

Blast from the Past

For all of her faults, and there were many, Margaret Hare, ran a fairly tight boarding house. For some reason that I never quite got to the bottom of, she was frequently referred to by the nickname Lucky. I suppose, in hindsight, that she had been relatively lucky in life. Logue, her first husband, had run the boarding house well in the past and upon his untimely demise it passed to her and she quickly took up with one of the young lodgers. Within weeks Hare reappeared in her life and the two of them set about running the house. Hare still engaged in agricultural work at harvest time, as we all did, and he took his horse and cart around the streets selling fish the rest of the time. When we stumbled across our alternative business Margaret insisted on regular payment from the doctor's money of £1 for doing nothing – Oh that I could have been that lucky.

However, I have to take my hat off to her for the boarding house. She had one large room full of beds where she fitted in as many people as she could. It only had 8 beds in it but at harvest times she could fit over 24 people in there, each happy to pay the 3d for a share of a fresh pile of straw loosely held together in what claimed to be a bed frame.

She never had any dodgy business going on in her house – anyone entertaining people in the rooms who were not paying guests were out on their ear. She was very clear that she was running a boarding house and not a brothel, which is somewhat ironic given some of the rumours I had heard about her.

Anyway, one such person who was thrown out was Mary Haldane. Mary Haldane had actually been a resident of the boarding house back when Logue was alive. She had been 'required' to leave shortly after Hare appeared at the establishment. Whenever I asked too many questions, the atmosphere got very frosty. There was more to that story than I knew about.

My separation from Hare did not last long. The draw of easy money pulled us back together within weeks. Given the history with Mary Haldane, I shouldn't have been surprised when Hare insisted on buying her a drink when we bumped into her one day when we were out drinking, burying our differences.

I don't know what age Mary was when Hare knew her but she looked old now. Maybe she hadn't aged well; maybe she had always looked haggard. It was unusual to find a pretty woman who made a living by prostitution. Pretty women had more subtle ways of relieving men of their money, in my experience. She was living on the streets now, eating scraps. She had lost most of her teeth except one of the front ones. I don't know if it was abnormally large or whether it was the absence of its fellows that made it look so. It certainly drew your eye.

Mary had three daughters. One was married to Clark the tinsmith who had a shop on the high street. She never heard from this daughter who had managed to climb up out of the gutter and wanted to distance herself as far from her mother as possible.

The second daughter had just been transported to Australia. I'm not sure what for – it was probably some petty stealing but apparently, according to Margaret, she was completely innocent and it was all a great miscarriage of justice.

I see quite a few Australians in my current location. They seem very relaxed people. Maybe it was a national mistake to transport all our petty criminals to a sunshine paradise. I understand some of my relatives even made it out there, voluntarily of course[1].

The third daughter was living on the streets as well and Margaret hadn't seen her for several months. Large families were an occupational hazard for the likes of Margaret, she was fortunate to only have three children. We spent the afternoon drinking in an establishment a good way away from our normal haunts, hoping we had less chance of Mrs. Hare finding us there. By the time the skies started to darken, Hare had found enough courage to suggest we continue drinking back at his house. As we approached he got cold feet.

"Where are you staying Mary?"

"Any doorway that I can find, you need to get off of the main streets so that you don't get moved on." She pulled her shawl around her shoulders.

"Well, our stable can be your place of rest tonight." He led her down the side of the house to the yard at the back and pulled open the door. "Obviously can't take her into the house", he whispered to me as we watched her settle down in the straw. He pushed the door shut and we turned and wandered back towards the front door. "Lucky wouldn't understand. She never did like the woman[2]."

"What's not to like?" The list in my head was long but there was no point starting an argument.

"Exactly, but Lucky is a jealous woman William. If I could think of a way of getting back in her good books and wiping out all my past indiscretions ….." He stopped and reached out and took my arm. "How drunk do you think she is?"

"Drunk enough." The plan might only just be forming in his head but I had seen it coming since we started heading home. A drunken old woman lying in the stable, nobody looking for her and it would suit Hare to demonstrate that she meant nothing to him. What better way to do it, and earn some money in the process!

Funny thing about the Haldane women - well maybe not funny from their point of view but curious I suppose - two of them were to cross my path.

Later in the year I came back to my room to be told there was a woman waiting to speak to me inside. I wasn't expecting anyone and that sort of meeting is not normally good news so I entered with a little trepidation. Lying on the bed was a middle aged woman, a little the worse for wear. No one seemed to have any idea where she had come from or why she was there. My first inclination was to throw her out of the house before Nellie came home but, by now, my evil business brain was taking over.

A drunk woman had just walked into my rooms – it seemed a little too good to be true[3].

There would be much speculation later as to whether Peggy Haldane had actually come looking for her mother or whether it was complete coincidence that she appeared on my door step. If she was looking for her mother then she was in the wrong place as her mother had been dispatched in Hare's stable. Hare would later claim that he had directed her to me as he could not confess to his wife that Mary Haldane had been in the vicinity. That may just have been a story to lay claim to half the money.

Either way, on that day back in 1828, I was simply presented with too good an offer to turn down. A drunk woman in my rooms, no witnesses and the easiest £8 I ever made. I managed to get a few mumbles out of her. I found out her name and that she didn't have a friend in the world. I rolled her over so that she was face down in the bed and I held her there. She didn't even flinch as the life drained out of her. Ironically, the one person I killed on my own and I didn't even use the method that we had perfected and would subsequently be named after me[4].

Chapter 11

The Path to Destruction

I mentioned that Effie was the first person we had ever killed that we had known for more than a few hours. We had a good system that had seen us in business for nearly a year. There were so many folk travelling in and out of Edinburgh and the streets were so crowded with people, especially in the Old Town that it was impossible to notice if someone went missing. We didn't have CCTV and proximity card readers that tracked your every move. I hear people complain about 'Big Brother' watching them but sometimes it is comforting to know that someone is there. Back then your big brother expecting you home would have saved you from me.

By this time we had killed over a dozen folk and no one had made even the slightest enquiry about any of them. It seemed so easy. For some time after we killed Effie I wondered whether other cobblers were supplied by her and would notice her absence. After a few weeks had passed I realised that, although I knew Effie, I couldn't really tell you when I saw her last. It wasn't like she had a regular route; she came and went and it became obvious that no one was going to notice if she 'went' permanently.

Some people you do notice.

Daft Jamie, and his side kick Bobby Auld, were regulars on the streets of the Old Town[1]. The two of them were as daft as brushes and used to be the brunt of jokes from many of the kids on the streets but no-one would ever harm them. Daft Jamie had fallen out with his mother and had moved in with his sister and her family in Stevenlaw's Close. He was on the streets of Edinburgh in all sorts of weather, barefoot and hatless but usually with a smile on his face and a joke ready for you. I was never one for riddles so I didn't have too many dealings with Jamie but I understand he often came out with the answer before you had had a chance to work it out. He was often given clothes and food by local people although he never directly asked for them. He was a well-known character in Edinburgh[2] – it would have been foolish to have anything to do with his disappearance, but, by now, we were being foolish.

I'm not sure why we kept at it. Maybe because it was easy money and nobody was stopping us. There hadn't even been any rumours that would have made us think twice. Each time we handed someone over to the doctors we got several months' wages. To be brutally honest, killing people was easy. Hare and I were hardened drinkers- we could drink most people under the table. We had mastered a routine. Take in some poor old person, give them so much to drink that they could barely stand and then I lay on top of them whilst Hare held their mouth shut and pinched their nose. It only took a few minutes and then we left them to their own devices to slip away. I was meant to stop them struggling but very few of them did, mainly because they were old and drunk.

It was October, starting to get cold, and I was drinking in Rymer's. There was nothing unusual in that. I started drinking shortly after breakfast and it had gone ten at this point. I was leaning on the bar in the back corner of the shop when Margaret Hare walked in. Her eyes darted around the shop, fell on me and then she moved away to get some provisions.

A few minutes later she appeared at my side.

"William, what a surprise! Are you going to get your old landlady a dram?" I signalled to Willie, Rymer's boy, that I would stand her a dram and threw a few coins across the bar. She made small talk for a few minutes, I honestly can't remember about what; I rarely listened to what she said. She then stamped on my foot, smiled and left. I assumed this was some sort of signal that I was wanted back at their house - Hare had found another victim. We didn't have an agreed signal. It was not beyond Hare to have found a victim and to be proceeding by himself- he had previous form in that department and, to be honest, it was not beyond Margaret Hare to simply stamp on my foot out of wickedness but I believed it was a signal. I let her have a few minutes head start and then waved cheerio to Willie and headed up the road.

"Oh, thank God you're here." I was almost dragged off of the street and in through the front door. "Hare needs your help."

"What's he got?" I asked, thinking Margaret seemed unduly concerned with our business. It was not like her.

"He's in the room with Jamie."

"Jamie?" I really hoped that I had heard that wrong.

"Aye, Jamie, Daft Jamie. I found him wandering the streets looking for his mother so I brought him back here for the two of you." She hustled me along the corridor to the back room.

"Are you trying to get us killed! Jamie! He's young and strong and…."

"And he'll take a drink like the rest of them." She pushed me through the door and I heard the key turn behind me.

It was the same small room looking out over the back yard, a bed in the corner and a fireplace, around which were sitting Hare and Jamie. He looked up as I stumbled into the room.

"I'm just waiting for my mother. Mrs. Hare said she would be here soon."

"Did she now?" I held out an empty glass towards Hare. If looks could kill it would have been Hare we were taking to the doctors that day. He filled it up without meeting my gaze.

"Are you not drinking Jamie?" I sat down beside him.

"No, I don't drink."

"What not at all? A little dram never hurt anyone." Hare held a glass out towards him. It contained more than a little dram. Jamie looked at Hare and then at me with the same childlike trusting eyes that haunted my sleep.

"Well maybe just a mouthful. But don't you tell my mother." He took the glass and barely moistened his lips. It was going to be a long morning.

What happened in that room that morning has of course been documented[3] – a complete web of lies in the actual indictment which Mr Hare chose to reinforce. He had me taking the major role, in fact the only role, while he just watched. He had me threaten him with violence, stabbing him if he didn't come and help. I've never stabbed anyone in my life. In fact, I've never threatened anyone with violence. I've been violent, don't get me wrong, but I never threatened anyone.

Jamie drank little more than a mouthful over the next hour and a half. He was getting restless as to where his mother was. Hare eventually persuaded him to have a lie down on the bed with the promise that she would be there when he woke. As he faced away from us on the bed we broke into wild gesticulations as to what we were going to do. We could have called it off but we were locked in the room. Margaret had probably put the key on the floor just outside the room. We might be able to reach underneath it and pull it through but you could hardly do that without arousing suspicion. Hare shrugged and went over to lie down on the bed.

"He hasn't drunk enough. It's too risky." I hissed. My old illness was playing up and I didn't feel up to a full on struggle with a youth.

Hare just smiled back and propped himself up on one elbow over the dozing Jamie. As he lowered his hand towards his face I positioned myself above his legs, ready to take hold.

I came away from that one battered and bruised. The thrashing legs of a twenty year old are not to be compared with the gentle tremors of an elderly drunk person. He fought for his life. It took nearly ten minutes before we finally rolled off him. I had been kicked away twice and had to relaunch myself at the legs as they beat around wildly in the air. Hare and I lay on the floor catching our breath as Jamie's slipped away from him. Part of me was grateful it was over but most of me was experiencing a heavy sense of doom. We had just taken on a fit twenty year old and won. Was there no stopping us now? Would we end up dragging people off the street? How could we be getting away with something so fundamentally wrong?

Jamie was distinctive. He walked everywhere barefoot and you could tell it by the state of his feet. He had a distinctive walk, as though something was not quite right with one of his feet[4]. He would surely be recognized by Knox's men when we dropped off the body. We took the clothes off and I bundled them up to take around to my brother. His two sons were running around in rags and the clothes would be welcome by them. Jamie's famous snuff box was pulled from his jacket pocket. Hare took the brass box and offered me the copper spoon[5]. I pocketed it that night but later, when I came to my senses, I got rid of it. McCulloch was on hand again to help us take the loaded chest around to Surgeons' Square where Paterson took the body in and gave us £4 telling us to come back the next day for the rest.

I heard after the trial that the body had been recognised by Fergusson, one of Knox's men, but all those learned men persuaded themselves that it couldn't be Jamie. When news got out about his disappearance the body was taken through the dissection rooms out of order, the feet removed, so by the time it got to the trial there was not a shred of evidence that could be found…apart from the clothes.

Richard and William fought over the clothes with Richard eventually swapping his share for a dog whilst Constantine was seen wearing Jamie's trousers by the very person who had given the trousers to Jamie. All of this came to light after my trial, people are very wise in hindsight.

I got three weeks peace after Jamie's murder. I refused to pay Lucky her £1 cut as I no longer lived in the house and I had been called upon to help her husband out[6]. I wasn't going to pay for the privilege of being kicked around by a 20 year old. She refused to speak to me for a whole three weeks. She wasn't the only lucky one that month.

Chapter 12

Two More Women

My new dwellings were on the ground floor, off an unnamed dark little alley between Weaver's Close and Grindlay's Close. The Broggans, from whom I was subletting, lived with us in a small room[1].

As you entered the building you were faced with a corridor, the Connoway's door on the right and the Law's door on the left. A little further down that corridor on the right hand side you came to another door that led to yet another corridor at the end of which was our little house. It was a single room with a window out into the back yard. We had a few chairs, a passable bed and a fire. What more did you need? The second corridor offered an unprecedented level of privacy for an old town tenement. At the time we were just looking to get out of the Hares' lodging house and Broggan had this room but it did mean that people were not disturbed by the noise of my cobbling - or any other noises that might come from my rooms.

There was a shop upstairs as well as the shopkeepers' room so there was a fairly regular footfall of people going in and out of the tenement. The Connoways were pleasant enough - Ann Connoway could be a little too talkative but her husband had spent time serving in Donegal so we often swapped militia stories over a dram or two. Janet Law owned the room opposite where she took people in as lodgers. She also took in people's washing and she was one of the few people around who owned a mangle. I think this contributed to the number of people coming and going out of our tenement - a mangle is a useful thing.

I should have taken more interest, what with Broggan's pregnant wife being some sort of distant relative of mine. I guessed that she must have

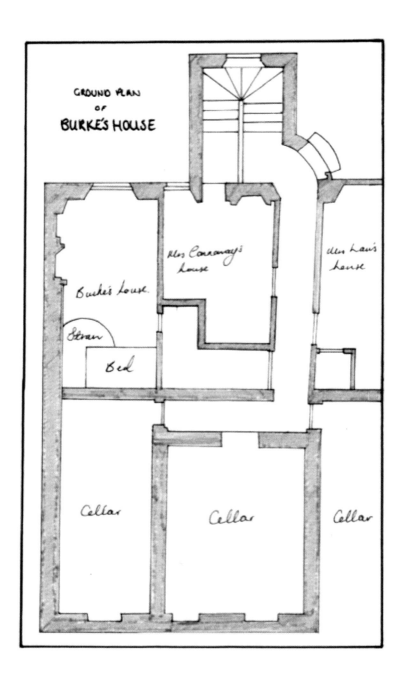

GROUND PLAN
OF
BURKE'S HOUSE

Mrs Connanay's house

Mrs Law's house

Burke's house.

Stair

Bed

Cellar

Cellar

Cellar

been at least his second wife as his other child was nearly 16, and also called John. That would be quite a gap between children nowadays but back then it was just unheard of. They seemed to have taken on a washer woman in the lead up to the birth as Mrs Ostler seemed to appear on a daily basis. She was the widow of a porter and made her living by taking in washing. It didn't seem to make sense that the Broggans had taken on a washer woman when Janet Law lived in the building and was a wash-erwoman herself. Mrs Ostler brought the washing she had taken on for other people with her when she came over to the house. I think she was coming to use Janet Law's mangle. Maybe the popping to the Broggan's was simply for a natter, rather than employment.

It was towards the middle of the week. Hare and I were returning home after a session at Rymer's. I knew that the Broggans were out so it was a surprise to see Mrs Ostler standing in the doorway waiting for the rain to ease.

"It's not going to stop for a while." I squeezed past her and into the corridor, "Why don't you come in and have a dram?"

"It's a little early for me" she tittered but turned anyway and followed me along the corridors, Hare bringing up the rear.

The fire was still smouldering from Nellie's breakfast. I had been out walking the streets since around 3am; I found it hard to sleep nowadays. I often took a bottle to sleep with me but sometimes even that was not enough to fight off the bad dreams and lessen the physical pain in my leg. With a quick fan and some fresh wood the fire was soon glowing. We shed our wet clothes and settled down with the bottle. For the first hour or so Mrs Ostler occasionally looked out of the window to see if the rain had eased but she eventually gave up. By lunchtime she was falling asleep and we eventually persuaded her that she should just go and lie down on the bed; we would wake her up when the rain eased off.

We never woke her up. Hare held her mouth and nose shut and she passed away without much of a struggle. She had ninepence ha'penny in her hand which we eventually managed to prise out of her fingers. We heaved the naked form of Mrs. Ostler in to an old tea chest I had in the cobbling corner of the room and pushed down the lid. It was still raining so we pushed the tea chest into the coal cellar and settled back down by the fire.

It was becoming automatic. We hadn't even discussed it - it was just assumed that if we drank with someone we would eventually kill them.

The rain eased off in the afternoon and we got the chest taken along to Surgeons' Square. We returned to Rymer's £8 and nine and a ha'penny richer.

Broggan made a comment a few days later complaining how Mrs Ostler had disappeared without even telling them that she was going away but there was no suggestion that anything untoward had happened.

Our summer trip to Falkirk had reacquainted us with Nellie's family. We must have invited them to Edinburgh because a few months later we received a letter from Ann M'Dougal saying she would soon be with us. Nellie called her her cousin but I think she was some relation of Nellie's previous husband, who wasn't really her husband anyway.

Nellie had been cleaning the room since the start of the week. I didn't know that stone floors could gleam.

I'd been persuaded to go and meet her at the coach drop off.

It was a damp day, not actually raining but there was a heavy mist in the air and you couldn't see the castle from Prince's Street. The coach was late. When Ann stepped down out of the carriage she looked so vulnerable and innocent that I felt some sort of primal urge and I had to remind myself that she was a guest in our house and some sort of distant relative. She stood out as a country bumpkin and I could almost see the pick pockets and ne'er do wells closing in from the side streets.

I waved, not wanting to approach her for fear of being bundled out of the way by the other ruffians, and she came across to me. She flung her arms around me and gave me a big hug. I wasn't expecting that.

"William, it's so nice to see you. This is all so exciting." I found it hard to match her enthusiasm, although I tried. I picked up her bag and trudged off back towards the Old Town. She followed behind, twittering away, something about the castle and the King[2] and all the things she had seen on her journey.

Nellie had a spread of food laid out for us when we returned. I sat for several hours letting the talk of the women wash over me as I worked my way through a bottle of whisky. It was a girlish laugh of Ann's that brought me back to my senses.

"You'll not mind will you William?" Nellie was waiting for my reply. I shrugged and looked blankly at them. "I was just saying that the bed is big enough for the three of us. We will just need to make sure you are not sleeping in the middle." I smiled what I hoped was a non-committal grin. Ann gave another girlish giggle and Nellie's face stayed set in stone. Did she not remember the last time we had three people in our bed? Maybe the beating had knocked it out of her.

"I'll get another pallet in the morning."

"Aye, that's maybe best." She smiled across at Ann but shot me a glance. Was it a warning? No, she knew better than that. Maybe it was a plea.

The momentary silence was broken by another woman coming in - she was John Broggan's wife. She was heavy with child. I got up from my chair and helped her down into the seat. John appeared behind her and another bottle of whisky was opened. I don't exactly remember when the Hares appeared but by the end of the evening we were all very merry. Eventually the flutes came out and the dancing began.

"You've done well William." Hare slid up beside me leaning against the fire place. "What does Broggan have to say about all this?"

"What do you think? He's not going to charge us more for having a visitor for a few days; he's behind on his rent anyway. We need to keep an eye on that, we guaranteed his payments after all." I drained my glass and stumbled off to refill it. Hare followed me.

"Will he not comment when she disappears?"

"Why would she dis…..Oh no, no, no. She's a relative."

"You hardly know her; you only met her in the summer." He glanced across the room at her. "If we keep this up for a few days then she will be putty in our hands."

I looked across at the women dancing and tried not to see just the money.

"You'll have to do it. It doesn't feel right, her being a relative."

"You just keep her drinking for the next few days and I'll be back when Nellie has gone out." We separated and spent the next few hours drinking even more. We had a similar party the following night. I'm not sure any of us sobered up between them.

The next morning Nellie got up and left early. She wasn't happy about leaving me and Ann in the same room. She tried several times to get Ann to go out with her but Ann was very much the worse for wear.

"Just leave her woman and go out."

"I could wait and go later." She started to take her shawl off again, for maybe the fifth time.

"Nellie, will you just go out. I'm not going to touch a hair on her head. Do you not trust me?"

"I know you William Burke. Tongue of silver and an eye for the ladies." She pulled the shawl back around her shoulders.

"For heaven's sake woman, she's a relative."

"Aye, a relative of mine. What about Lizzy, she was a…."

"Get out!" The empty bottle smashed against the door as she yanked it shut behind her. It would be hours before she was brave enough to venture within 20 feet of me after bringing up the past like that. We had our window of opportunity.

I probably could have taken care of Ann on my own. She was slight and still drunk from the night before. I went over to the bed to see how far gone she was. She stirred a little, opened one eye and smiled.

"Oh William, back in your bed." She didn't seem unduly concerned about my being back on the bed with her. In fact….no, I must be misreading the signs. I went back over to the far side of the room and sat down to wait for Hare.

Hare arrived around mid-morning. He walked in very business-like.

"Right, are we needing a dram?" He rubbed his hands together looking from me to the bed and back again.

"I don't – I've had a few already." I heaved myself up from the chair.

"I was talking about Ann." He reached over and took the bottle from me.

"I don't think you'll wake her up to get her to drink." I'm not sure she had been sober since a few hours after she arrived.

"Good." He walked over to the bed and to be honest I hadn't realised that he had started until he called over for help. I lowered myself down onto Ann's body, squashing out her breath. I could feel her squirm a little beneath me, but not in the way I had imagined over the previous two days. In less than five minutes she was as limp as when we had carried her to the bed the night before. I never had made good on my promise of another pallet for her.

Hare climbed off the bed and went over to the table for a drink. I rearranged the bed so it looked like she was sleeping in case Nellie decided to come back.

"I popped into Rymer's on the way here but they have no tea chests at the moment so I had to get a trunk from Paterson" He sat down and lifted his feet up onto the table.

The trunk from Paterson was a very grand affair. Ann's body fitted easily inside it and we propped it up in the corridor outside the room whilst we waited for nightfall. We usually tried to go to Surgeons' Square in the dark. The first time we had gone in the middle of the day, with Mary Paterson, we had been followed by a crowd of children shouting that we had a body in our bag. No one had paid them any attention but there was no need to take more risks than necessary[3].

As we were sitting at the table, chatting away, the door opened a crack and I could see the distinctive face of John Broggan looking in.

"Ah, you're here." He opened the door wider and gave the trunk a tap with his foot. "Whose is this?"

"It's mine. I've got to deliver it on this evening." I walked over to get him a glass from the kitchen area and held it up with the unspoken question of 'drink?' He nodded.

"It's an awfully fine trunk. I didn't realise you had gone into the delivery business."

"You make your money where you can." Hare pulled out a chair for him.

"You two never seem short of money. I thought Nellie had some legacy."

"She spends as much as she brings in." I downed my drink and poured another. Hare shot me a glance over the table. How long had Broggan been in the corridor before he opened the door? Had we left anything hanging out of the trunk? Had he actually opened it? Did he know what was inside it? He glanced around the room, a slow measured look – as if discreetly checking something in particular but trying to conceal the fact.

"Has Ann gone?" My blood ran cold. He knew, I was sure in my bones that he knew that she was inside in that trunk. My eyes met his and we looked directly at each other for a long time.

"She's gone off to Glasgow." Hare said, thankfully remembering her plans that had been discussed in front of us all. "I think she just couldn't bare sleeping with William anymore." He gave John a nudge and let out a laugh. It was only at that point that the eye contact broke. "He's got an awful loud snore."

"She left very sudden." John turned around to look back at the trunk which we could all see through the open door. Hare and I shot each other glances across the table behind his back. He went to pick up the whisky bottle by the neck, presumably thinking of knocking John out with it whilst he wasn't looking. I grabbed the bottom of it and pulled it back down onto the table.

"Landlord was in looking for you again John." Time to try another tactic.

"It's been hard getting out to work with the wife about to have a child." He turned back around and took a shot of whisky.

"Remember I am the guarantor on your rent." Hare smiled, his cheeks falling in to give him a hideous appearance.

"I know, and I appreciate it gentlemen, but it's hard finding the money this month, especially with the child on the way."

"We," Hare pointed between me and him, "could maybe ensure your rent was paid this month."

Broggan finished his drink and placed the glass down onto the table.

"That would be very generous of you indeed. I take it that your delivery business is bringing in a little extra income." The gaze came up to meet mine again.

"It has its moments."

"A good delivery can get us £10." Hare smacked his lips as the dregs of his drink disappeared over his thin lips and into his mouth.

"£10! What the hell are you delivering? No, don't tell me. I don't want to know." Broggan got up from his seat and took a few steps backwards. "Are you in this together then?" He looked from Hare to me and back again. You could almost see the cogs working. £10 a delivery, £3 outstanding rent.

"So, how much is the rent, £3 isn't it." I reached into my pocket and pulled out some money. I looked across at Hare. "£1 10 shillings each?" He nodded and produced some money from his pocket.

I pushed the coins across to Broggan who grabbed them off of the table[4].

"Thank you, gentlemen that's very kind of you." He gave us each a quick nod. "You will make sure you take that box away?"

With that John Broggan left the room and we never saw him again, or our £3. The scoundrel left without settling his rent bill. Some people have no honour.

Chapter 13

The Final Victim

Mary Docherty - our downfall. Well, actually communication was our downfall but more of that later.

Mary Docherty was our final victim, the only one for which I was tried. I was not found guilty of 16 counts of murder; I was found guilty of one. Of course, one is all it takes when you have capital punishment. I was guilty of the other 15 and I duly confessed to lighten the load on my soul but Mary Docherty is where it all went wrong.

'It was, I think, God's providence that put a stop to our murdering career. I don't know how far we might have gone, maybe even to attacking people on the streets'[1]. We had got away with it for so long that we thought ourselves invincible. I think part of me wanted to get caught to bring it all to an end. After all this time to think about it, it is the only way I can justify my actions either side of the arrest.

It was Halloween 1828. We had had the Grays staying with us for a few days. Extra rent was always welcome but these people hadn't really been paying their way. This was overlooked however as Ann Gray was some relation of Nellie's former husband - although he was no more her husband than I was. Ann's husband, James, was originally a jeweller but he had enlisted with the Elgin Fencibles then moved to the 72nd regiment and they had just returned to Edinburgh after 17 years. They were meant to be staying with us whilst they sorted out other accommodation but it had been a week now, they had a young child and I was getting a bit fed up with the arrangement. I was drowning my sorrows at Rymer's.

An old woman came in and asked Willie Noble if there were any scraps that she could have. She had some sob story about coming all the way over from Glasgow to find her son. She had missed him down in the Pleasance by only three days as he had moved on and she was now returning to Glasgow. An old woman, alone and about to embark on a journey across the country; no one would notice if she disappeared, and her Irish lilt gave me the perfect conversation opener.

"That's a long journey to start on an empty stomach, will you join me in a drink?" I laid the accent on a bit thicker than normal and a wide smile spread across her face.

"I couldn't turn down a fellow countryman." She took the glass and held it in her hands for a minute before sipping the whisky. I got the whole story about her son, the previous night in the Pleasance and her trek back to Glasgow. From her dress I guessed she was a recent arrival in the country. It turns out she was from Donegal.

"I know Donegal. I've still got family there."

"Really? Maybe I know them, I'm Mary Docherty."

"Docherty, that's my mother's name![2] We must be related." I drained my glass. "I'll not let a relative leave town with an empty stomach. Come on home and I'll get my wife to give you a proper meal." And with that she took the first step towards her demise.

By the time we arrived back at the house I had persuaded Mary that she should stay for a fortnight and find her son. It was silly to return to Glasgow when she had only missed him by a few days. If he was working locally on the harvest then he was bound to reappear within a few weeks.

When we got inside Nellie went to make breakfast and help Mary with some washing. She wouldn't eat anything until lunchtime as it was a Friday, a Catholic tradition I had given up a long time ago, so I left the women to it and went off to find Hare.

After a few trips between the White Hart Inn[3] and Rymer's I bumped into Hare. I told him about the old woman. By now we didn't even need to discuss what we were going to do. It was a given that anyone in our company would eventually end up at Surgeons' Square. It was Halloween, a party would be expected and I had the feeling Mary Docherty would not be averse to a few drams.

By the time I got back to my house it was dark. Mary was sitting by the fire supping porridge, Nellie was over in the kitchen area and Ann Gray was clearing up around the bed, a nasty habit that was to prove troublesome later.

"Ann, you'll see we have company." I nodded towards Mary.

"Aye, Nellie was telling me, some relative of your mothers?"

"That's right. The thing is I can't really ask her to stay elsewhere, what with her being family."

"It's a bit late for us to be finding somewhere else." She seemed a bit put out by the request, anyone would think she was actually paying rent.

"I've spoken to a friend of ours around the corner, he has some space and could take you in. It's just for the night." I should have said that a bit more quietly as I had told Margaret she could stay for the fortnight.

"Is it because it's Halloween?" She continued as I stared at her blankly.

"Well yes, there will be a party and I need the space for Mary. You and your husband can go and quarrel around at the Hares'."

"You're a fine one to talk about quarrelling…" I turned to stare her straight in the face. She gave in and lifted up the pile of clothes from the bed. "I'm ready."

We walked around to the Hares' where Margaret Hare was more than willing to take them in and make them comfortable.

For none of the other murders had we undertaken so much planning. We usually bumped into someone, or Margaret Hare had lured them in, we had a lot to drink and then we murdered them. For Mary Docherty there was nearly a day of planning. She was invited into the house and made to feel comfortable. She went out that afternoon and chose to return. I had had to move three other people out of the house to clear the stage for the drama that was about to unfold that night. The coldness which the operation had taken on chilled me and I stayed out drinking and making preparations until around 10pm that night. Hare had been entertaining all three women; Nellie, Mary Docherty and his own wife. He told me later that they had spent most of the evening at Ann Connoway's, one of my neighbours. When he had tried to get them all back into our house Mary Docherty had refused to move until I arrived back, claiming she didn't feel safe without me present. That doesn't say much for her judgement of me but speaks volumes about her perception of Hare.

When I arrived back everybody moved into our house, Mary hobbling a bit as she had hurt her foot dancing at the Connoway's. The dancing continued, there was much drinking and I even got out my flute and played a bit. Mary's first language was Irish Gaelic and I amazed myself with the ease with which I slipped back into my mother tongue. Eventually the drink got the better of Hare and he said something. To be completely honest with you I can't even remember what it was. It was probably just some snide remark about me but with the amount of drink I had in me the one comment was all it took for me to fly off the handle. I landed a punch on him and he hit the ground. The stunned look on his face soon turned to anger and he was back up and laying into me like a punchbag. Hare was cunning and evil, a scheming devil in breeches but in a straight out fisticuffs I could take him, even though he had over a decade on me[4]. Mary Docherty run off down the hallway crying 'Murder'[5]. Our wives hadn't moved an inch, having seen this sort of thing on many occasions but now they set off down the corridor and pulled her back into the house. Bless her soul, Mary Docherty tried to break us up. Even I wouldn't have tried to get between two men fighting like us. She soon got pushed out of the way. Hare had had enough and stepped back from the fight. Casting a glance over my shoulder he made a lunge for the stunned Docherty on the floor and before I knew it our plan was put into action. Hare held her mouth and nose shut whilst I stopped any thrashing around. There was none. She slipped away and we slipped back into our drinking, the fight forgotten. The women had left the room as it became obvious what was about to happen. I knew that Margaret Hare was aware of what we were doing, well she had the cheek to charge me £1 per body but in hindsight I was deluding myself that Nellie hadn't worked it out for herself.

Hare and I stripped Docherty, split the 7 shillings she had in her pocket, and trussed her up under the straw at the end of the bed. We were so depraved at that time that the four of us continued drinking in that very room, in fact John Broggan junior even joined us.

It was November and the days were cold but even in that weather a dead body soon gives off an odour. I had gone to see Paterson the night before but he hadn't been home when I was there just before 10pm and when I called again at midnight it was too late to do anything. Around 9am the following morning he sent his younger sister, Elizabeth, around with a message that I was to get in touch with him about the delivery[6].

I went around to Hares' with the message and stumbled in on the Grays. They had heard all the details of the party. They felt a little excluded as Halloween celebrations seemed to be a particularly Irish thing. Ann Gray told me she had left the child's stockings at our place and before I knew it they were following me back round to my house for breakfast. The whole day produced a series of events beyond my control.

Once inside the house I discovered that the neighbours had been in asking about Mary and her whereabouts. I was met by a lot of knowing looks.

"I was just telling Janet and Ann about that Mary Docherty." said Nellie. "I kicked her out for being a bit to free with you."

"Well, I'm an attractive man, what can I say?"

"That silver tongue of yours will be your undoing William Burke." Anne Connoway left the room not knowing how true her words would become.

"Well, if your relative is away we could move back in here." Mrs Gray sat herself down and lit up her small clay pipe. "The Hares are very welcoming but there is something about that Mister Hare that is a bit…." She didn't finish the sentence. It was hard to put a word on the feeling that you got when you looked at Hare.

The women washed and prepared food and I sat in the room staring at the pile of straw and trying to convince myself I couldn't smell the decaying flesh. I spilt whisky on the bed, on the floor, at one point I tripped over the stool and even managed to get some on the ceiling. In hindsight, it must have looked very strange.

John Broggan junior reappeared and joined me in the drinking.

Suddenly, I jumped to my feet.

"What are you doing woman?" I shouted. Ann Gray stopped and stared at me, bent double at the side of the bed, about to reach under the covers.

"I'm missing a pair of stockings for the child, I told you at the Hares."

"Well, they're not there. Check over in the corner where you left all of your other rubbish." I sat back down, poured another drink. I needed to get out to see Paterson and arrange the removal of the body but with so many people around the house it was going to be difficult. Maybe half an hour passed before I yelled out again.

"What are you doing woman? You can't be that near the straw with a lit pipe. Are you trying to burn down the house?"

"Away with you! We need the potatoes." Ann Gray reached under the bed and pulled out the sack of potatoes. I swear she must have been within a few inches of the body. I couldn't take any more.

I moved the remaining stool over towards the bed, sat John Broggan down on it and told him not to leave until I got back. Just to make sure, I left him the remains of the bottle of whisky.

It was somewhere between 5 and 6 pm when Hare and I returned to the house. We had stopped at Rymer's for a drink and arranged for a tea chest. Mary Docherty was still under the bed, covered in straw, so we pulled her out and squeezed her into the chest, tying the lid down before we went to get McCulloch, the trusty porter. When he arrived he pushed in the few locks of hair that were sticking out of the box and with a knowing smile hauled the box up onto his back.

"Surgeons' Square is it lads?" We nodded and set off on our usual route. Nellie and Margaret Hare followed a little way behind us. They had seemed rather agitated when we had got back to the house. It seemed that John Broggan was as useless as his father and had left the house shortly after I had. Ann Gray had then had a poke around under the bed and found the body. She had taken Nellie to task about it. They were making such a commotion about it that, when Margaret Hare appeared on the scene, she had persuaded them to all go to the inn to discuss it. The outcome was that the Grays were still intent on telling the police so we had to remove the body as soon as we could. Nellie and I had to put our heads together and come up with a story about when Mary Docherty had left our house. At that point I was confident that we could outsmart the police.

We arrived at Surgeons' Square and Paterson let us into the room to drop off the box. He didn't have any money on him but was confident that Knox would want the body. He suggested we all go along to Knox's house. It was not the usual course of events but a brisk walk to Newington did not seem out of order for £5, with another £5 to follow on Monday once the doctor had looked over the body.

Knox had a grand house in Newington, fine front garden and large windows which he would regret having once the mob broke them all[7]. Paterson disappeared into the house and the five of us relocated to a nearby public house to wait for him. The women were still concerned about the Grays. Hare and I dismissed it. There had been rumours before. We had a front as ressurectionists. We never lifted a body from a grave, but it explained the odd hours, the packages and any strange behaviour. People didn't tend to ask too many questions if they thought that was your trade. We were confident the police would dismiss it as sour grapes from a dislodged tenant[8].

Paterson came back with the money. McCulloch got 5 shillings for his trouble and probably wished he had never seen us again. Hare and I split the rest getting 2 pounds, 7 shillings and 6pence each[9]. We stayed for a few drinks before heading back to the West Port just before 8pm and met a man outside the house asking for me. He introduced himself as Sergeant Major John Fisher.

"Can you tell me what has become of your lodger, Mr. Burke?"

"I can. He is standing right beside you." I pointed at Gray who was standing just behind the policeman. "I had to turn him and his wife out for bad conduct. Have they been telling spiteful stories?" The look on his face told me that he thought this probably was a storm in a teacup and he had better things to be doing with his time.

"If we go inside we can maybe clear it all up." He followed Nellie and me into the house, leaving Gray out on the street. He made a beeline for the straw, moving it around and looking at the bed sheets. "What happened to Mary Docherty, the woman who was here last night?"

"She was here last night. I had to move the Grays out; I needed the space and the two of them were always arguing and not paying their way - I was using Mary as an excuse to get them out. She stayed here drinking all night. She got a bit wild and Nellie threw her out. "

"What time would that have been?"

"Around 7am."

"And these blood marks?" He pointed to the bed sheets.

"They were from a previous woman." Nellie had been hanging around the back of the room but now stepped forward with her explanation. "I haven't got around to washing the sheets yet, we have had that many guests."

"Did you know Mary Docherty before this weekend?" The Sergeant Major led Nellie off to the other side of the room so it was hard for me to hear what she was saying although if everything was going to plan she should have been saying that she knew her well, had met her since the incident and she had apologised for her behaviour.

"And what time did you ask her to leave your house?"

Nellie paused for a moment.

"Around 7......pm."

"Well, Mr and Mrs Burke, would you like to come with me."

Chapter 14

Court

Nellie and I were arrested on the 1st of November and put into separate cells. I wasn't too concerned about things at that point. The net was certainly beginning to close around us but there was little evidence for the police to go on. On the 2nd the police had gone along and recovered the body from Knox's rooms and a whole chain of people had identified it as the woman who had last been seen in our house. The Hares were arrested that day.

On the 3rd of November I was taken in to see Sheriff Tait to explain what had happened. It's at this point that I think my senses started to leave me, although it may have been an effect of sobriety, not something I had experienced much in the last few months.

Sheriff Tait seemed like a reasonable man so I started with the truth. I had got up at 7 o'clock on the Saturday morning and had started mending a few shoes. Gray and his wife were already up, Nellie got up a little later and we all had breakfast. That evening I told the Grays they had to leave because they weren't paying their way. As I sat there I think I began to realise the truth was not going to work – I was guilty. I was going to have to come up with something else. So I said that around 6pm, while I was out drinking, a stranger approached me and asked if I knew where he could get some shoes fixed. I took the man back to my place and, while I was fixing his shoes, he asked me if he could store a box in my house. I said that would be all right and he went away, returning with a box which he seemed to unpack at the end of the bed, I had been sitting with my back to him so didn't see exactly what he was doing. I finished fixing the shoes and he left. I had then had a look in the box and discovered the body. When the stranger returned I had insisted that he had to move the body. He said he would take it away but not until Saturday night. It was my intention to reveal this stranger as being Hare, who hadn't been mentioned by anyone up to that point.

On Saturday morning I met the woman, who was a relative and she came back for breakfast. She left to go and beg in the town. The stranger, who I now claimed was Hare, came back with McCulloch and they took the body away, paying me for storing it. The woman never returned. There was blood on the bed but it was Nellie's from where I had struck her.

Nellie knew nothing about the body. Clearly she did but I wanted to try and protect her. I honestly believed that she had only just found out about my side-line.

Of course all this story really amounts to is a big boy did it and ran away. The times didn't match up, it made no sense and, considering the time I had to think about it, I should have come up with something better.

On November 10th we were committed to stand trial and I found myself again in a room with the sheriff. He read the statement back to me. At this point I thought a story slightly closer to the truth might be better. Claiming I never knew Hare was going to be easily proved incorrect in court. We had spent most of the last year living in the same house and were frequently seen out drinking together.

I told him that the events that I had said happened on the Saturday actually happened on the Friday - Halloween. That had been when I had met the woman and she had come back for a Halloween party. At some point during the night Hare and I ended up fighting. When we were separated, we couldn't find Mrs Docherty anywhere. We searched the house and found her in the straw at the end of the bed, dead from drink. The women left the room as they didn't want to deal with dead bodies. Hare and I had panicked and thought we could dispose of the body by selling it to the doctors. We had crammed her body into an old tea chest, which took some force and would explain any marks on the body. It was fairly close to the truth. It would have been even better if Nellie had changed her story too, but she wasn't to know I had changed mine[1].

We were on fairly safe ground. People had seen the woman come into the building, we had an explanation as to how she had died and no one but Hare and I were in the room when it happened. They could suspect all they liked but it was going to be very hard to prove what happened behind closed doors. Very hard that was until the 29th of November when Hare turned King's Evidence. Even after all these years it's hard for me to speak calmly about what that bastard did to me. He killed me. If he had kept his mouth shut then it would have been impossible for them to find us guilty. On the other hand, I was sick, my illness was causing more and more issues. Maybe he did me a favour; a quick death rather than slowly rotting away. Why Did Hare do it? I don't know. Why didn't they ask me? I don't know[2]. I've had some consolation over the years to know that he probably came to a sticky end himself[3].

On December 1st Hare made his declaration to the sheriff. On the 8th the indictment was published[4] and the lawyers appeared.

We were not short of lawmen. Despite their number I'm not sure any of the lawyers were particularly interested in getting us released. Their main concern seemed to be getting one over on the judges[5]. It seemed Nellie and I had walked into a political situation that wasn't really any of our concern[6]. We couldn't afforded lawyers ourselves but the Scottish system provided legal aid. Usually it was the lowliest lawyers trying to cut their teeth on the legal cases of the poor but the big guns had been wheeled out for us[7]. My team was led by the Dean of the Faculty; Sir James Moncrieff, assisted by Patrick Robertson, Duncan McNeill and David Milne[8]. Nellie's team was led by Henry Cockburn along with Mark Napier, Hugh Bruce, George Patton[9]. Although they did come and see me a lot of their case had very little to do with me. Time wore on towards December 24th, the trial date.

Every dog has his day and this cur was to get his day in court. A whole 24 hours. We didn't have comfort breaks or months of adjournments back then; the trial lasted for a whole 24 hours and everybody stayed in the court room for that entire time with the windows open and the rain coming in.

Nellie and I had been brought up to the court house the day before, for fear of a riot. I heard they had brought extra police and soldiers in just for us. It was a bit daunting that the whole city was on high alert just for us. I was thankful we were under arrest and surrounded by police as I'm sure that if we had been released into the street the crowd would have ripped us limb from limb. Mind even the Edinburgh riots were not what they used to be[10]. From my current museum case I can see across the room to the most famous riot rouser of Edinburgh; Joseph Smith. Joseph was a fellow cobbler. He died before I arrived in the town. He fell from a carriage whilst returning from a day at the races in 1780[11]. I understand drink was involved.

He hangs in a case by the door. Just as well he hangs as if he stood on the floor I wouldn't be able to see him at all. He was only 4 foot tall and his leg bones are all bent, giving him the nick name of Bowed Joseph. Back in the 1770's he could raise a mob of 10,000 in less than an hour. If he had been alive that week I might not have made it to the gallows.

That day, the court room was crammed full of people, I don't think I had ever seen so many people in one place, all clamouring for a view of us. They certainly had their opportunity as we were led into the court just after 9.30am and had to sit there for a full 40 minutes before the judges came in.

There were four judges sitting at the front, the Right Honourable David Boyle seemed to be leading the proceedings and he was flanked by Lord Pitmelly, Lord Meadow and Lord Mackenzie. At the time they were simply nameless faces but you tend to remember the people who kill you. The prosecutor was Sir William Rae, the Lord Advocate. He was aided by Archibald Alison, Robert Dundas and Alexander Wood.

Before they even read out the indictment our lawyers were on their feet objecting[12]. The judges pointed out it was unusual to object before the indictment was read out so they went ahead and read it and our case entered legal history as well as social history.

The indictment against me was on three charges; the murder of Daft Jamie or James Wilson to give him his proper name, Mary Paterson and Mary Docherty. Nellie was only mentioned in the Docherty case. There was no connection between the three murders, apart from me obviously, and so the lawyers argued that there shouldn't be an indictment that tied all three of them together. Nellie's lawyers argued that she could not be tried under that indictment as she was only involved in one of the murders and to mention her in the same indictment as two murders with which they were not claiming she had any involvement would prejudice the jury against her. The lawyers spent nearly an hour discussing it. Eventually the judges came down on the side of our lawyers and told the prosecutors that they would have to confine themselves to one of the charges. They chose the Docherty case as it was the only one that mentioned both of us.

Bear in mind that at this point Hare had turned King's Evidence and had given them information about all three murders. He had confessed to two murders which were not going to be tried in court. This would come back to bite him later on.

The jury was selected, 15 men; a manager of an insurance company, two builders, three merchants, one banker, one agent, three grocers, an engraver, an ironmonger, a brewer and a cooper. As the hearing started I paid close attention. At this point I had more or less accepted my outcome. I knew I was guilty, I wasn't expecting anything less than the death sentence. I was interested as to how it would all unfold. It was a strange sense of detachment that I experienced that day. The only feeling holding me in that room was a slight shame that Nellie was there with me, and a slight embarrassment that there was no shame for the 16 people who were not alive because of me.

With only one murder being tried the witnesses were cut from 55 to 18[13]. Docherty's body had been retrieved and so they didn't need to talk to anyone from Knox's anatomy school about the bodies that had passed through the system. This is where the accusations of a medical cover up spring from.

The first witness was James Braidwood. He had made a drawing of my house and was simply there to verify that the drawing in court was the one he had made and that it was a true representation of my house. You couldn't argue with that.

Next up was Mary Stewart. I had never seen this woman before so was interested in what she could possibly add to the proceedings. It turns out that she owned the place where Mary Docherty stayed the night before although she called her Mrs Campbell, or Madgy, or Duffie. There was an awful lot of vagueness in the court and our lawyers picked up on it. She had been called in to identify the body and also identified the clothes that were there in court. Unfortunately we hadn't got rid of those quickly enough so they were found in our house.

Next up was a man by the name of Charles McLachlan. He confirmed what Mary Stewart had said and admitted to walking up the road with the woman to the foot of St Mary's Wynd. He had identified the body and clothes as well.

William Noble was next to take the stand. He was the shop boy at Rymer's. My heart took a bit of a leap as William might have overheard an awful lot in Rymer's. He could certainly confirm we had purchased a number of tea chests from them. In the end he confirmed that I met a woman there and that I took her away for breakfast. He said I came back on Saturday and bought a box but that I didn't take it away. Mrs Hare had been sent to fetch it for me. Although he was just telling the truth I thought it was nice that he had linked the Hares into it.

Ann Connoway, our nosy neighbour was next. She confirmed the lay-out of the house and they took some time establishing which was her room and its position in relation to our room. She identified myself and Nellie as the people who stayed in the room. She said she had seen the woman eating porridge in the house that afternoon. She saw her later and dissuaded her from going out to find her son as she was a bit the worse for wear. The woman had then stayed in her house talking away to her husband about Ireland. Hare had arrived with his wife and Nellie and all four of them had been in there dancing and drinking until I had got home later that night. She hadn't really heard much that night but came in for breakfast the next day, and she linked in Elizabeth Paterson who came to find me that morning. She had met Mr Gray at the house that afternoon but she had not gone in and seen the body as she was too scared. Her husband had asked me about it that night but I had apparently laughed and defied all of Scotland to say anything against me. I don't remember that but the chance of me having been sober at that point was slim. Maybe I did say it[14].

Janet Law, our other neighbour, confirmed the story adding a few particulars about Nellie borrowing her bellows and a dram glass. She had a bee in her bonnet about us not returning things.

Hugh Alston was next. He owned the grocery shop directly above our house and he also had the rooms above the shop. He had heard someone shout murder and went looking for the police but hadn't found anyone. By the time he came back it was quiet so he went back to bed. He had been more concerned about a fire than a murder, thinking it would affect his shop; murders were not such a concern.

Elizabeth Paterson appeared on the stand confirming her age and the fact that I went around to see her brother. For all it added to the trial you would have thought they could have saved her the trouble. I was to discover later on that the fact that I had spoken to her before we had murdered Mary Docherty showed intent. Maybe all our planning had not been so wise.

David Paterson then appeared. He was being very coy and understandably so as he could easily find himself mixed up in this. He confirmed that I had been to see him at midnight and told him I had a body for the doctors. He came around to the house but did not see the body. He said that he had told us to deal with the doctor but admitted that he and Jones saw us at the doctor's rooms that night and went to Newington to get the money for us. There was great debate over how the money was split and who exactly gave the money to us. Whether it was all given to me and I gave some to Hare or whether it was split by Paterson. It was obviously some legal point, the importance of which I was not aware of, but the Lord Advocate clearly was aware and complained that the cross examiners were going off the point. Paterson confirmed that the police had arrived the next morning and had taken the body away. It had not been unpacked and was still squashed into the tea box.

John Broggan junior was next. He looked like he really did not want to be in a court. John had already had dealings with the police for assaulting women and wanted to be as far away from this case as possible. He confirmed he arrived at our house around 4pm and that all of the people mentioned were there. He confirmed he left and that he reappeared around 2am. He stayed in until 7am and then left for a couple of hours coming back at 9am. That last outing would have been the time that I told him he had to stay on the chair and not let Mrs Gray anywhere near the bed. If he had just done what I had told him to we could all have been spared this. At least the lawyers didn't appear to be paying any attention to the story reported in the Edinburgh Evening Courant on the 6th of November that Broggan had actually been the murderer[15].

The Grays came next, Mr and Mrs. They told the same story although they filled in some of the blanks that Nellie and Margaret had glossed over when they had explained it all to me. They said I had been acting suspiciously around the foot of the bed. Mrs Gray said that Mrs Law's serving girl was in the room at the time they discovered the body and that when they had found the body they had packed up and left the house as quickly as possible. They bumped into Nellie on the way out and she had begged them not to say anything, offering them money to keep quiet. I had given Nellie a quick glance when that came out. Did she not realise that offering them money to keep quiet meant that she must have known what was going on? Margaret Hare had then appeared and they had all gone to the inn to talk the situation over. The Grays then went to the police. I hadn't realised there had been quite so much discussion with the Grays, or that Nellie was quite so aware of what was going on.

James McCulloch was next on the stand, and was as edgy as Paterson had been. He had followed me to the house and had seen the box. He started off stating he had no idea what was in it but eventually the lawyers got him to admit that he was aware it was a body. He confirmed that he had pushed some hair into the box and that it needed some force to keep the lid down. He had carried it to Surgeons' Square and from there went to Newington where he had got paid. The big discussion about who exactly paid him was repeated.

The next man was the policeman who had come to see me that Saturday; Fisher. He confirmed that he had come to my house with Gray and another person called Findlay. He confirmed that I had said I had never seen the body that they showed me, either alive or dead.

Next came the star of the show; Mr Hare.

He took the stand in a very cocky manner, grinning from ear to ear. He was reminded that there were limits on the protection that he had under King's Evidence and then he was sworn in as a Roman Catholic. I don't remember him ever attending church in the entire time I had known him. I suppose he could say the same for me, although there had been a time when I attended regularly. At least he wasn't excommunicated like myself.

There were times during his evidence when I couldn't help but smile. The cheek of the man that he could stand there and tell bare-faced lies in the court, and on his honour as well; but then we all know what honour meant to him!

The Lord Advocate started with him and they spent a long time going over exactly what I said to him when I met him in Rymers. Did I use the word shot or did I use the word murder? I never used the word murder at all and eventually after much debate they came to the same conclusion. Next he told a story that obviously wasn't true but didn't do him any great favours either. It had me murdering the woman on my own whilst he sat and watched. He then came across to Newington with me and we each got 2 pounds, 7 shillings and 6 pence. A very specific amount and correct to the penny.

Then Cockburn got up from his seat and so began the next hour of arguing the point.

'Have you ever been connected to supplying the doctors with subjects upon other occasions than those you have spoken of?' The Lord Advocate was on his feet straight away objecting. Hare was removed from the room.

It was pointed out that Hare had turned King's Evidence and could not be tried for anything that he had confessed to. Clearly he could be tried for anything he hadn't confessed to and that he admitted in court. Cockburn wanted to demonstrate to the jury the quality of the man they were dealing with. They agreed that Cockburn could ask the questions but that Hare did not have to answer them.

Hare was brought back in. He was reminded that he was under oath and then it was explained to him that if he admitted something in court that he had not confessed to them he would have no protection and so he needed to think carefully before answering any of the questions put to him. Cockburn started what turned out to be a bit of a solo performance, asking Hare questions and then asking if he would rather not answer. Each time he chose not to answer he essentially confessed.

The Lord Advocate objected again and Hare, by this time looking a little bemused, was removed again. The lawyers launched into another debate which was beyond most of the people in the court. Eventually Hare returned and was asked a few more questions before being dismissed.

The next witness was Mrs Hare. She came to the stand with her child, seeming to care for it much more than I had ever witnessed in the past. It had whooping cough which seemed to flare up each time she was asked a question. She told the same story as Hare although she did let slip that she had ' seen such tricks before'. She confessed that she had left her husband three times. They must have been very short absences as I had never noticed them and Hare had never mentioned them. Maybe they were before we met them. She even had the cheek to suggest that she was scared that she and Nellie would end up murdered. The flaming woman suggested we murder Nellie!

She was followed by the three doctors, Dr Black, Dr Christison and

Dr Newbigging. They all stated that they thought the woman had died of violence although when cross examined it was established this was based more on personal feelings than on hard medical facts. They struggled to explain whether it looked any different to suffocation from nonviolent means. The spinal ligaments were damaged but even the doctors suggested that that could have been caused by placing the body in the box.

With that the case for the prosecution finished. We didn't have any defence and so they simply read our declarations out to the court. If I hadn't realised it before then the declaration being read out in court certainly demonstrated how weak it was. It was embarrassing to sit and listen to it. It made no difference, I was guilty, I wasn't expecting anyone to believe my story.

The Lord Advocate summed up the case. I thought it was unnecessary for him to remind the jury that there had originally been three murder charges but my lawyers didn't object so I suppose they must have thought it was going to make little difference at that point. Our lawyers took over and concentrated their attack on Hare. The only damning testimony came from him and as they put it,

'What, if that ruffian who comes before you, according to his own account, with his hands steeped in the blood of his fellow creatures, breathing nothing but death and slaughter; what if that cold blooded, acknowledged villain, should have determined to consummate his villainy, by making the prisoners at the bar the last victims to his selfishness and cruelty. What is there to restrain him? Do you think he is incapable of it?'

Without the Hares there really was no case, which was why they had needed them to turn King's evidence.

The jury left at 8.30 that Christmas morning. The next 50 minutes were the longest of my life so far.

Nellie looked much shaken. Not surprising I suppose when you are on trial for your life. I tried a quick smile across to her and said to keep her eyes on me when they read out the verdict. She wasn't bearing up very well under the strain.

50 minutes later the jury returned and John Mair, the foreman stood up.

'The jury find the panel, William Burke, guilty of the third charge in the indictment; and finds the indictment not proven against the panel, Helen M'Dougal.'

It was what I had expected.

'Nellie, you're out of the scrape.' A quick smile to the weeping woman at my side and then back to listening to the three judges summing up the case. They discussed at length the possible outcomes, deciding in the end that the only option was death. Nellie was drowning in her tears beside me. I'm not sure why she cared quite so much for me in view of the way I had treated her most of our lives.

The Lord Justice Clerk summed up the case. What he said that Christmas Day will forever be remembered in history.

'William Burke, you now stand convicted by the verdict of a most respectable jury of your country, of the atrocious murder charged against you in this indictment upon evidence which carried conviction to the mind of every man that heard it, in establishing your guilt in that offence. I agree so completely with my brother on my right hand, who has so fully and eloquently described the nature of the offence, that I will not occupy the time of the court in commenting any further than by saying that one of a blacker description, more atrocious in point of cold blooded deliberation and systematic arrangement, and where the motive was so comparatively base, never was established in the annals of this or any other court of justice. I have no intention of detaining this audience by repeating what has been so well expressed by my brother; my duty is of a different nature, for if ever it was clear beyond the possibility of doubt that the sentence of a criminal court will be carried into execution in any case, yours is that one, and you may rest assured that you have now no other duty to perform on earth but to prepare in the most suitable manner to appear before the throne of Almighty God to answer for this crime, and for every other you have been guilty of during your life. The necessity of repressing offences of this extraordinary and alarming description precludes the possibility of your entertaining the slightest hope that there will be any alteration upon your sentence. In regard to your case, the only doubt which the court entertains of your offence, and which the violated law of the country entertains in respecting it, is whether your body should not be exhibited in chains in order to deter others from like crimes in time coming. But, taking into consideration that the public eye would be so offended by so dismal an exhibition, I am disposed to agree that your sentence shall be put into execution in the usual way but accompanied by the statutory attendant of the punishment of the crime of murder – viz that your body should be publicly dissected and anatomised and I trust that if it ever is customary to preserve skeletons yours will be preserved in order that posterity may keep in remembrance your atrocious crimes. I would entreat you to betake yourself immediately to a thorough repentance and to humble yourself in the sight of Almighty God. Call instantly to your aid the ministers of religion of whatever persuasion you are; avail yourself from this hour forward of their instructions, so that you may be brought in a suitable manner urgently to implore pardon from an offended God. I need not allude to any other case than that which has occupied your attention these many hours. You are conscious in your own mind whether the other charges which were exhibited against you yesterday were such as might be established against you or not. I refer to them merely for the purpose of again recommending you to devote the few days that you are on the earth to imploring forgiveness from Almighty God.'

With that speech delivered he slipped a black cloth on his head and continued,

'The Lord Justice Clerk and Lords Commissioners of Justiciary in respect of the verdict before recorded discern and adjudge the said William Burke panel, to be carried from the bar, back to the tollbooth of Edinburgh, therein to be detained, and to be fed upon bread and water only, in terms of the Act of Parliament passed in the 25th year of the reign of his Majesty King George II entitled 'An act for preventing the horrid crime of murder. Until Wednesday 28th day of January next to come and upon that day to be taken forth of the said tollbooth to the common place of execution in the Lawn Market of Edinburgh and then and there between the hours of eight and ten o'clock before noon of the said day, to be hanged by the neck, by the hands of the common executioner, upon a gibbet, until he be dead, and then his body thereafter to be delivered to Dr Alexander Monro, professor of anatomy in the University of Edinburgh, to be by him publicly dissected and anatomised in terms of said act; and ordain all his movable goods and gear to be escheat and to be brought to his Majesty's use, which is pronounced for doom. And may Almighty God have mercy on your soul.'

The evidence didn't carry conviction to the mind of every man who heard it – two of the jury voted for not proven.

Chapter 15

The Final Drop

It will come as no surprise to you, I hope, that I do not want to dwell for too long on what happened during the following month and I have no intention at all of going into the details of events at the end of January; public displays and riots that you can read about in any paper of the time[1]. In fact, with my trial and execution, there were 8000 extra copies of papers sold around that time.

For those of you who are wondering how I can tell this story now; I have to confess I do not know. I assume I am bound to the earth somehow as a penance for the acts I committed. I know there was great debate at the time about whether, if I truly repented, I would be allowed to enter Heaven. The more pious wanted me to be eternally condemned while religious men realised there was a flaw in their talk of an all forgiving Lord. Surely there had to be a point of no return? And surely I had over stepped that mark. An interesting question but, as an excommunicated Roman Catholic, not one that was high on my list of concerns. Rather like in a bad accident I did black out for a while. I died as a man and I woke as a skeleton. The process between the two is a blank that I was not present for, thankfully, but it is well documented.

I was taken down from the court room to the cheers of the crowd and placed back in the cell I had been in. At that moment I fell to my knees and prayed. Maybe I wouldn't have been so quick to do that if I had fully understood the Murder Act and realised that in Scotland I would have 30 days to contemplate my transgressions.

I was torn at that point. When Hare turned King's Evidence I knew that it was likely I would be found guilty. I had mounting health problems – testament to my younger carefree days. It was certainly bad enough that the doctor would end up persuading them that I needed to be fed more than bread and water for the next month if they wanted me to be kept alive[2]. If I hadn't been found guilty then I would have slowly rotted away without the medical care that you take for granted these days. Maybe it was a blessing in disguise, a very good disguise. I had had a faith. I had been quite ardent in it before I met Hare and I used to carry a Bible around with me every Sunday. With nothing to do but dwell on my mistakes and the only company being prison guards and religious men it seemed only right that I spend the next month reapplying myself to my forgotten saviour. I took advice from both the Roman Catholics and the Protestants, reverting to my army days when I attended any service that was going. Although, back then, it was to meet the ladies more than it was to save my soul.

On Friday morning at 2 o'clock they decided to move me to Calton Hill prison and the condemned cell. It was a bloody cold place. I assume they did it at such a ridiculous time because there was still the possibility of a riot and the mob lynching me in the street. The condemned cell was slightly more comfortable than the cell at the court house but I still had to wear irons on my hands and feet. I was constantly in the presence of one of the prison guards due to an off hand comment I had made before the trial about how much better it would be if I just ended it all[3]. Quite how they thought I was going to commit suicide whilst chained in a locked cell I am not sure but they certainly went to great lengths to ensure that I survived the month of January. I talked with that guard. We discussed the inaccuracies in Hare's story and, although I denied having anything to do with Jamie's death, I eventually confessed to him that I had been there, although I always stuck to the line that Hare 'had persuaded me to join him and now he has murdered me; and I will regret to the last hour of my existence that he did not share the same fate[4].'

I prayed that Nellie would find the path away from the evil that I had introduced her to over the last few years. She and Constantine came to the prison to try and see me. They were not allowed in but I sent my watch up so that she could sell it and get some money.

I mused with the guard that Knox really ought to pay us the outstanding £5. We had a deal after all and it wasn't my fault that he had handed the body over to the police. We had supplied the body and he hadn't paid the full fee. In hindsight it seems a bit of a strange argument I know but I was in shabby clothes and less than a month away from making the biggest public appearance of my life. I wanted to look respectable.

I was interviewed in my cell by someone[5] - he wanted to know how I had turned from the church to murder. I gave it some thought and then admitted that I just did not know. Maybe it was because I had become addicted to drink, I was living in open adultery, associating with abandoned characters that I gradually became hardened and desperate. I had given up attending mass and I had shunned the face of the priest, being constantly familiar with every kind of wickedness.

He asked how long we had been murdering people and I told him we had started in December 1827. He asked how many people we had murdered - the story on the streets was that we had murdered over 30. I smiled and told him it was nowhere near that many although at that point I had not counted them up. I confirmed for him that I had only ever done one myself, all the rest had been with Hare and they were all by suffocation[6]. I had only ever worked with Hare, no one had taught us. Arguably we were encouraged by the fact that Paterson would always take the bodies. I took his eager note taking as an opportunity to reiterate that I had never been a resurrectionist. The suggestion had been allowed to linger in the court case, seen as being the lesser of two evils and creating a reason for there to be bodies in the house; an excuse for anything Nellie had seen.

On January 3rd, after considerable discussion with all of my religious advisors I made a full confession in front of Sheriff Tait, the Procurator Fiscal and the Assistant Sheriff Clerk. I was fed up with the constant visits from people asking for details about the murders. I thought if I gave a full confession then I might be left in peace. It was only then that the true scale of our deeds came to light although the confession was not published at that time. There were still proceedings developing against Hare.

The lawyer for the Wilson family came to see me to ask if I would assist in the prosecution of Hare and I was only too happy to say that I would.

Thoughts went back to my wife in Ireland but I was told that she was aware of what was happening and had no desire to communicate with me[7].

I had managed to get word out to a writer, Mr Smith that I wanted to tell my story. He applied twice to the Lord Provost to come and see me and was refused[8]. I ended up making a fuller confession which I planned to get out to him. I was to be betrayed until my dying day as the fellow prisoner I gave it to, a man by the name of Ewart[9], did not pass it on to Mr Smith. Instead he gave it to one of the turn keys called Wilson, who ended up giving it to the editor of a paper, the Courant. I'm sure money must have changed hands. The initial deal was that the confession was not to be published until three months after I had died. I understand it ended up being published a lot sooner. The day before my execution I wrote a note[10] saying that Mr Smith should collect the confession from the paper as he was the originally intended recipient. I even got Bailie Small and Reverend Porteous to watch me sign it[11]. I understand he never retrieved it from the paper but they came to some agreement[12].

I spent most of January praying and reading the Bible. There wasn't a lot else to do. I was moved to Liberton Wynd jail at 4 o' clock on the morning of the 27th of January. They still seemed to think there was danger of a riot and that the mob might try to attack me. I spent the rest of the day with Father Reid and Father Stewart, the Roman Catholic priests, and then with Reverends Porteous and Marshall, the Protestant ministers. I slept very soundly that night, despite the construction noise outside. I was up at 5 o' clock the following morning. I didn't need the last £5 from Knox as they gave me a black suit to wear and finally they removed the irons that had restrained me since I had been sentenced. It was a relief to know that I was going to look presentable on that final day.

At half past six the Catholic clergy arrived again and I spent a full half an hour with Father Reid. I prayed for all I was worth, which I suppose some would argue was not much. After that I went through to the keepers' room where they had lit a nice warm fire. I sat down in the chair beside it and stared at the flames, lost in my thoughts. Bailies Small and Crichton came in and the clergy went through the final religious exercises. It was strange to be so aware of the last rites being read. Whenever I had heard them before it had been over some ageing relative, dazed in the final moments on their death bed. I had previously said that I would not accept a pardon even if it were offered[13]. At that point I might have changed my mind.

As I left the room I met Williams, the executioner. We had met before when he came to measure me up. I told him I wasn't ready for him yet but he followed me into the room and set about pinioning my arms. He looked at the neckerchief I was wearing. He was clearly trying to find out how it was fixed so I helped him out by telling him it was fixed at the back. At this point, arms restrained, I was offered a glass of wine! Bailie Small helped me drink from the glass. The room was beginning to fill up as magistrates entered and I felt the time had come to thank all the people who had looked after me for that last month. Bailie Small had been particularly attentive and we had had some very good discussions but there were also the other Bailies, Mr Rose, the Governor of the jail, Mr Fisher, his deputy, both of whom had been to see me as well as Mr and Mrs Christie the lock up caretakers. Eventually I could delay it no longer and it was time to leave.

Bailies Small and Crichton led the slow procession up Liberton Wynd. I was supported by the Catholic priests as it is surprisingly hard to walk when your arms are restrained behind you. As we approached the top of the road, the roar of the crowd seemed to swell and swell. I was helped up the steps and I looked out on that crowd with astonishment. There must have been thousands of folk there, maybe even tens of thousands. They lent from all the windows overlooking the area and stretched as far as my eyes could see up the Royal Mile. They were all there to see me - to see me die.

The view of the crowd was blocked out by the familiar figure of Father

Reid.

'Right son, repeat after me..' I sank to my knees and I repeated his words although I had no idea what I was saying. The crowd shouted out things.

'Burke him! You'll soon be seeing Jamie! Where's Hare? Where's Knox?' The words washed over me and I stared around, trying to hear what the priest was saying. People complained that the priest was blocking the view. The words stopped and hands helped me to my feet. The priest picked up the hanky I had been kneeling on and put it into my hand. He lent forward to speak directly into my ear.

'Remember son, repeat your creed and give the signal when you say Lord Jesus Christ. Die with his blessed name on your lips.' I nodded my head and he stepped out of the way. There was a noise behind and Williams appeared with the noose. He started trying to remove my neckerchief but he was feeling around at my throat for the knot.

'The knot's behind[14].' I reminded him. The neckerchief disappeared and the rope took its place. I felt it tighten. He placed the hood on my head and started to lower the edge. I gave a quick shake of my head. It was an instinct to try and keep the view, any view, for a little longer. The hood came down and I was faced with whiteness. I shut my eyes and started the creed.

'Lord Jesus Christ....' I dropped the hankie.

Don't trust priests. In 1829 you did not die immediately on hanging- that was not the goal of the process. I dropped maybe a few inches and hung suspended above the hole. My legs instinctively lashed out and I was sent spinning. The cheers of the crowd drowned me and the pitying eyes of the young boy came back to haunt me.

Lord Jesus Christ might have been the last words on my lips but not the last thought in my head.

Notes

As soon as you start researching the story of Burke and Hare you come across the same issue that the Lord Advocate discovered in 1828; there is very little evidence. Historical research has the advantage of Burke's confessions and many[1] have pointed out that he had nothing to lose at this point so why would he not be telling the truth, but he also had nothing to gain. At the point of the confessions, Hare was still in custody[2] and Burke is on record as saying if he could make sure of the hanging of Hare he would die happy[3]. Those people who saw Hare's confession, most notably Sir Walter Scott, seemed to be of the opinion that they did not differ in any material facts[4].

For that reason I have used Burke's confessions, both the official and 'the Courant'[5] versions as the basis for this story, supplemented with facts from numerous other publications (listed in the bibliography) and documents from the National Archives of the United Kingdom, the National Records of Scotland, the Edinburgh City Archives and those held at the Lothian Health Service Archive and The Centre for Research Collections at the University of Edinburgh.

Where all biographers agree on the facts I have not referenced them all, reserving notes for the places where they differ. Where I have favoured one version of events, my reason for doing so is explained in these notes.

---

[1] Every book on the Burke and Hare trials has expressed an opinion about the reliability of the document, in fact Burke himself says that the declaration made before the sheriff is 'the only full statement that can be relied upon'. Original note on confession. Roughead, 1948. Burke and Hare.

[2] Hare was not released until the 5th of February 1829, 8 days after Burke's execution – Roughead, 1948. Burke and Hare.

[3] Roughead, 1948. Burke and Hare. Page 151.

[4] Roughead, 1948. Burke and Hare. Foot note on confession, Appendix 1. Also letter at front of confession to the Lord Provost Page 261.

[5] The Courant was a local newspaper that 'obtained' a more in depth confession. It is the source of many of the details of the case.

Notes on Chapter 1 – My Current Prison Cell

1 - Chapter one finds the skeleton of William Burke inside its case in the Anatomical Museum of the University of Edinburgh. Considerable research was undertaken to ascertain the date at which the skeleton first appeared in the University collection. Biographers are split between the older documents that state that the body was salted and preserved in barrels[6] and more recent publications that state that the flesh was stripped from the bones straight away[7]. Some wrongly state that the skeleton hangs at the Royal College of Surgeons'[8]. According to inventories of the University Anatomy collection the skeleton is present in the Goodsir Collection[9] in 1846 although the pages of the book on which it is written bear the watermark of 1852. The skeleton was present when the Anatomy Museum relocated to the new medical school in Teviot Place in the late 1870's[10].

2 - The glass roof had leaked for many years[11].

3 – Since 2012 the museum has opened its doors to the public on the last Saturday of each month but is used at other times as a student resource centre for medical and anatomy students. In 2015 the Anatomy Museum was in the process of updating its inventory with a view to a planned move to Hill Square.

4 – Contained within the display case are the life masks of Burke and

---

[6] Leighton, 1861. The Court of Cacus, note 18 Page 235, MacGregor, 1884. The history of Burke and Hare and of the resurrectionist times, page 178, Roughead, 1948. Burke and Hare, page 66.

[7] Knight, 2007. Burke and Hare, page 95 and Bailey 2002. Burke and Hare – the year of the ghouls, page 118.

[8] Knight, 2007. Burke and Hare, page 84.

[9] Centre for Research Collections. University of Edinburgh.

[10] The college building of the University of Edinburgh during the eighteenth century, in Medical teaching in Edinburgh during the 18th and 19th centuries. Matthew H. Kaufman. Published by the Royal College of Surgeons.(2003)

[11] Private communications and personal experience.

Hare, taken whilst they were in Calton Jail[12], and the death mask of Burke. There are two references to the death mask being taken. One is in Leighton (1861), that mentions a sculptor, Joseph, that was present at the private viewing before the dissection to take a mask for a bust and the second is in Adam (1972) stating that a 67 year old Marie Grozholtz, better known as Madame Tussard, was in the crowd at the trial and took the mask 3 hours after his death – this would be the day before the private viewing.

5 - Spelling was not as important in 1829 as it is today. It is possible that Burke wrote his name in a number of ways. The official confession is signed Burke, with an 'e'. The Courant confession where he wrote his name at the bottom has no 'e'. It is documented that Burke's first language was probably not English and the ease with which he conversed with the last victim in Irish, lends itself to the belief that his first language would have been Irish Gaelic. According to Edwards (1980)[13] the mute e does not exist in the Irish Gaelic and so it is unlikely that Burke would have used it.

There is also a hand written note in the 1831 MacKenzie catalogue of the Anatomical museum that shows a catalogue entry for the "Skeleton of a man, Burk".

---

[12] Adam, 1972. Dead and Buried: The horrible history of bodysnatching, page 87. Hand written note in Anatomical Museum archive gives the details of the Sculptor who took the life masks – See Note 3 Chapter 3.

[13] Edwards, 1980. The true story of the infamous Burke and Hare, page 58.

Notes on Chapter 2 - Disposing of the Dead

1 - At this point it is worth taking the time to confirm what we know of Burke's origins. It is stated in his Courant confession that Burke comes from Orrey in Ireland. This appears in most biographies, although Knight (2007) places him from Strabane[14]. Edwards (1980) highlights the fact that there is no place in Ireland called Orrey[15] and suggests that the mistake in the confession results from confusion over the fact that there is an Earl of Cork and Orrery which the transcriber might have been aware of. Also, given Burke's Irish accent the pronunciation of Urney might well have been misheard as Orrey. Urney is only 2 miles from Strabane.

2 - Nellie was the commonly used name of Helen M'Dougal and Burke is noted as using it during his trial, with the famous comment made after the sentences were passed, 'That's you out of the scrape Nellie ' which is found in almost every book on the subject. She was born in Redding and met Burke whilst he was working on the Union Canal construction work.

3 - Burke retrained as a cobbler, but he had had a number of professions. He started his employment with a Presbyterian minister which may be where he developed his ecumenical stance. He had been educated in a Catholic School in line with his family's religious beliefs so by the time he reached his late teens he would have been exposed to both religions. He left the employment of the minister to become a baker and from there he moved on to train as a weaver. Not finding his calling in either of those professions he then enlisted with the Donegal militia, at the age of 19, where it is claimed he was probably a fifer[16]. However, the records for the Donegal Militia, available at the National Archives of the United Kingdom, list the drummers and fifers on a separate page to the rest of the company. There are three William Burkes present in the militia dur-

---

[14] Knight, 2007. Burke and Hare, page 18.
[15] Edwards,1980. The true story of the infamous Burke and Hare, page 3.
[16] MacGregor, 1884. The history of Burke and Hare and the ressurectionist times, page 47, Edwards, 1980. The true story of the infamous Burke and Hare, page 20.

ing the early 1800's and they all appear on the standard solider pages. He served for 7 years spending most of the time as an officer's gentleman. He left the militia when it was disbanded and shortly afterwards appears in Scotland as a labourer working on the construction of the Union Canal. His training as a cobbler appears to have taken place whilst he was living in the 'beggar's hotel' belonging to Mickey Culzean.

Burke then relocates to Peebles for a few years where he works on the roads before returning to assist with more harvesting. Burke followed agricultural work around and we have stories that place him at a public house in Balerno after a shearing in autumn 1827 and at a harvest in Penicuik[17]. It is after this final harvest that he meets Margaret Laird (Hare) and is persuaded to move into her lodging house rather than to move down south and set up as a cobbler.

4 - Burke makes a reference here to the possibility of having children. It seems to be a commonly accepted fact that Burke did have children, the number varies. According to Thomas Ireland (1829) he had seven children, some of which were still born and 'all but one of them are now dead.'[18] To have produced seven children in the short time he was in Ireland seems unlikely. There is no mention of children in his relationship with M'Dougal and some stories[19] play upon his reported testicular cancer as something that would have stopped any attempts at having children, although we have numerous accounts of his infidelity[20]. There are other newspaper reports[21] that state he had two children, who both died. Burke predates the time at which it became obligatory to record births and deaths. Tracing Irish ancestors is notoriously difficult due to the de-

---

[17] Leighton, 1861. The court of Cacus, page 78, Bailey, 2002. Burke and Hare the year of the ghouls, pages 36 and 124.

[18] Ireland, 1829. West Port Murders, page 174.

[19] Bryd, 1974. Rest without peace. Although it should be noted it is very much a 'story'.

[20] We find accounts of infidelity, although all a little sparse on facts, in Leighton, 1861. The court of Cacus Pages 72-74, Douglas, 1973. Burke and Hare: The true story, page 28 and Edwards, 1980. The true story of the infamous Burke and Hare, page 91.

[21] An account of the last moments and execution of William Burke of Edinburgh for the West Port Murders. – Centre for Research Collections. Edinburgh University.

struction of many of the records. The vast majority of pre 1922 records were destroyed in the Irish Civil War by a fire at the public records office. Prior to 1922 many records had already been destroyed by order of the British Government. The census data of 1861and 1871 was destroyed shortly after it was taken and the census data for 1881 and 1891 was pulped during the First World War[22]. After extensive research no direct descendant of William Burke has been identified.[23]

5 - Effie appears here as a character that sells Burke bits of leather to help with mending shoes. She will reappear during the story. She was a street hawker who rummaged through fire cinders gathering scrapes that could be sold on. The information we have on her comes from Burke's confessions.

6 – Burke states in his confession that he previously knew Margaret Laird. Hare had also been a lodger at the house when Margaret's previous husband Logue had been alive. There is speculation that Hare had to leave the house after his advances towards Margaret were discovered by her husband. The husband then dies and Hare reappears. Whilst this might have seemed very innocent at the time it is maybe worthy of further investigation knowing what we know now about Hare's character[24].

7 - The debt of £4 seems odd. The cost for a bed was 3d a night therefore a debt of £4 would be the equivalent of 320 nights' lodgings, nearly 11 months' rent and yet the pension is quoted as being quarterly so surely some of the debt should have been paid off last quarter. For there to be a debt of £4 the Hare's must have been lending Donald money for something as well as not charging him rent.

8 - Hares character is maybe best demonstrated by a story told by one of his contemporaries, James McLean, who told Charles Kirkpatrick

[22] www.bbc.co.uk/news/uk-northern-ireland-27205043
[23] Personal communication rupparti@gmail.com
[24] Edwards, 1980. The true story of the infamous Burke and Hare, page 69.

Sharpe that Hare was of a 'ferocious and tyrannical disposition'. During the summer of 1828 he was returning from a harvest at Carnwath with Hare and Burke when they stopped at a public house in Balerno, near Currie. 'The reckoning being clubbed, Hare snatched up the money from the table, and put it into his pockets, when Burke, fearing lest a disturbance should take place in the house, paid the whole amount. After they left the inn Mclean observed to Hare it was a scaly trick to lift the money with an intention to affront them. On this, Hare knocked the feet from under McLean, and when prostrate on the ground, gave him a tremendous kick in the face. His shoes being pointed with iron plates, commonly called Caulkers, he wounded McLean severely, laying open his upper lip.'[25]

9 - Resurrection was the name given to the removing of dead bodies from graves, also referred to as grave robbing and the related act of body snatching whereby rival gangs of grave robbers would steal from each other. Edinburgh grave yards are full of mort safes and watch towers demonstrating the precautions people would take to prevent recently deceased relatives being removed from their graves. There are several publications, both old and new, which state that Burke and Hare started their career as grave robbers.[26] This was not the case and Burke goes to great lengths in his confessions to point out that that was never the case. At the time he was trying to implicate Hare. If he could have truthfully laid the lesser crime of grave robbing on Hare it seems strange that he denies that either of them were ever involved in such an activity.[27] The impression that he was involved in the selling of dead bodies was used in the court case as an explanation of why there might have been a dead body present in his house.[28] This built a defence for M'Dougal as finding a corpse in

[25] Buchanan, 1829. The trial of William Burke and Helen M'Dougal before the High Court of Justiciary at Edinburgh, page xiv. Bailey, 2002. Burke and Hare – the year of the ghouls, page 124 and page 36, Leighton, 1861. The Court of Cacus, page 78.
[26] Conaghan and Pickering, 2009. Burke and Hare, Notes Chapter 1 page 2.
[27] Original Confession.
[28] Buchanan, 1829. The trial of William Burke and Helen M'Dougal before the High Court of Justiciary at Edinburgh, page 153.

the house could now be explained. Whether it was deliberately done to provide M'Dougal with a defence we will never know.

The demand for bodies came from the requirements for anatomical teaching which is addressed in note 13 below. There were a number of grave robbing teams operating in the Edinburgh area. The main ring leaders were Andrew Lees known as Merry Andrew or Andrew Merrylees, 'Spune' and 'Moudewart'. Tales of their exploits can be found in Leighton (1861) and they are also mentioned by Lonsdale (1870). Many lecturers and students also turned to grave robbing to ensure they had subjects on which to practice including Liston[29] and Hunter[30]. Vesalius himself, the father of modern anatomy, was sentenced to death by the Spanish Inquisition for stealing a body.[31] There does seem to be some debate about how dead this body actually was, which might have been more of an issue. In fact the idea that doctors were directly involved in the trade is reflected in Robert Louis Stevenson's 'The Body Snatcher'.

10 - Almost all biographers have Hare depicted as taking the lead in the plan to sell Donald's body to the doctors. It must be remembered that the source of the information comes from Burke's confessions and his wish to implicate Hare. We will never know which man was the instigator of the idea. I have suggested it was Hare because it was he who was owed money and therefore more likely to come up with a plan to recoup it. Considering the split of the money, some suggest[32] that it is more likely that Burke instigated the plan and gave Hare enough to cover his debt.

11 - The source of most comments about Hare's physical description ap-

---

[29] Leighton,1862. The Court of Cacus, page 23, MacGregor, 1884. The history of Burke and Hare and of the resurrectionist times, page 27, Kaufman, 2005. Exhibition catalogue to commemorate the 300th Anniversary of the Chair of Anatomy, page 24.
[30] Moore, 2005. The knife man: Blood, body-snatching and the birth of modern surgery.
[31] Lonsdale, 1870. A sketch of the life and writings of Robert Knox the anatomist, page 111.
[32] Douglas, 1973. Burke and Hare: The true story, page 33.

pears to be from Blackwood's Magazine[33], written by Christopher North, which was the pen name of Professor John Wilson, the Professor of Moral Philosophy at the University of Edinburgh.

'Hare was the most brutal man I have ever seen. His dull blackish eyes, one rather higher than the other; his large thick or rather coarse lipped mouth; his high, broad cheekbones and sunken cheeks, each of which when he laughed – which was often – collapsed into perpendicular hollows, shooting up ghastly from chin to cheekbone – all steeped in a sullenness and squalor not born of the jail but alive to the almost deformed face. The leering miscreant inspired not fear for the aspect was scarcely ferocious but disgust and abhorrence, so utterly loathsome was the whole look of the reptile.'

It is safe to assume he was no oil painting some texts even go as far as to suggest that his appearance scared off some potential victims[34] referencing the fact that his eyes were on different levels[35]. Hare's life mask is in the anatomical museum at the University of Edinburgh so his general appearance is easy to assess. His eyes are normally spaced so whilst there may have been some facial exaggeration by way of the eyebrows there was nothing fundamental wrong with his bone structure. His nose is very prominent, narrow and pointed and it is believable that his cheeks might hollow if his mouth moved. Obviously his mask is expressionless and a large amount of evil can be conveyed by the eyes.

12 - The existence of this medical student is mentioned in Burke's confession. The University owes a debt of gratitude to this student. Had he not directed them to Surgeons' Square then the infamy of having dealt with Burke and Hare might rest with the University rather than Robert Knox.

---

[33] Blackwood's magazine was a monthly magazine published in Edinburgh between 1817 and 1905. Its archive is available on line. www.onlinebooks.library.upenn.edu/webbing/serial?id=blackwoods

[34] Bryd, 1974. Rest without peace, page 22.

[35] Douglas, 1973. Burke and Hare:The true story, page 30, Bryd, 1974. Rest without peace, page 10, Bailey, 2002. Burke and Hare – the year of the ghouls, page 33, Knight, 2007. Burke and Hare, page 16.

Medical teaching at this time was a complicated affair and explained fully in Matthew Kaufman's book (2003). The University, which had built its reputation during the leadership of Monro primus and his son, Monro secundus, was in a period of decline. The anatomical teaching was delivered by Monro tertius who was not an inspirational teacher and simply read from his grandfather's notes, even to the point of referencing events prior to his own birth. Students found it hard to learn from him and drifted towards the numerous extracurricular anatomists that had schools around Surgeons' Square. These teachers advertised that they had numerous cadavers from which students could learn.

The medical student and his redirection of the pair is often missed from the story[36]. I include it here as a reminder as to how close the University came to being involved in the whole grizzly tale, although I would like to think that had they knocked on the University's door, they would have been turned away[37].

The nameless medical student is credited by Edwards (1980) as 'saving the University from the worst crisis in its existence.'[38]

13 - The legal supply of fresh cadaveric material was limited to a few bodies a year and yet the total supply needed for all the anatomists in the city was over 300. It was this demand that pushed the rise in resurrectionists. In fact in the very year that Burke and Hare were operating the students petitioned for more bodies to be supplied.[39]

14 - The names John and William are found in the books used in Knox's room for recording the delivery of subjects[40]. Other body snatchers appear to be referred to by their own names.[41]

---

[36] The incident does not appear in Leighton's The Court of Cacus, where Burke and Hare appear looking for Dr Knox and encounter one of his students. A lot of the future stories are taken from this text. The encounter with the student appears in the confessions.

[37] I am frequently deluded.

[38] Edwards, 1980. The true story of the infamous Burke and Hare, page 81.

[39] Petition held in the Centre for Research Collections Edinburgh University.

[40] Echo of Surgeons' Hall, 1829. Douglas, 1973. Burke and Hare: The true story, page 33.

[41] Lonsdale, 1870. A Sketch of the life and writings of Robert Know the anatomist, page 102.

15 - Knox is described by Henry Lonsdale (1870), a former student of his as 'spotless linen, frill and lace and jewellery redolent of a duchess's boudoir, standing in a classroom amid osseous forms, cadavers and decaying moralities, he was a sight to behold and assuredly never to be forgotten.'[42]

16 - Knox's strange one sided appearance might have had little to do with the lamplight. Knox was blind in his left eye as a result of a case of small pox he suffered as a child. It is described[43] as disfiguring him although the exact details of the disfigurement are not detailed.

17 - Although it may seem strange that the anatomists asked for the shirt to be removed, this relates back to the resurrectionists. The act of removing a body from the grave was not actually against the law. However, the stealing of a shroud or burial clothes was. As novices to this trade, Burke and Hare were not aware of their error in leaving the shirt on the body. The anatomists clearly were aware and asked for it to be removed before they accepted the body, circumstantial evidence that they were used to dealing with grave robbers. All of the subsequent murder victims were stripped bare before delivery.

18 - The line said to them as they left the building that night features in the court case and the confessions. Was the fact that they were told by the anatomists that they would be 'happy to see them again' active encouragement to go out and collect more bodies? It certainly was not discouragement. Much is given to the fact that the anatomists never asked where the bodies came from. One would like to think the anatomists were not stupid men. They would have known the number of bodies needed to supply anatomy teaching was much greater than the number of bodies supplied by the town. This implies that they must have been used to dealing with grave robbers and those relatives and friends who needed

---

[42] Lonsdale, 1870. A sketch of the life and writings of Robert Knox the anatomist.
[43] His appearance is covered in any book mentioning Knox as it was a distinguishing mark which cannot be overlooked.

to dispose of recently dead relatives. This first case of someone who had clearly died of an illness would have raised no suspicion.

Notes of Chapter 3 - Crossing the Line

1 – The sculptor was Samuel Joseph, according to a note in the Anatomical Museum archive. He went on to become a founding member of the Royal Scottish Academy in 1826.

2 – Phrenology was considered a science that tried to explain how the mind works. It had four main principles:-
The brain is the organ of the mind.
The mind is split in faculties each controlling a different part of the personality, localised into an organ of the brain.
The size of the organ is based on the energy of that faculty.
These differences in organ size are reflected on the skull so that by feeling the head you can obtain information on the personality[44].
Phrenology is now seen as a pseudoscience with the last meeting of the Edinburgh Phrenological Society been held in 1870.
Burke played a part in the downfall of phrenology when Thomas Stone published a paper in 1829 looking at Phrenological observations based on his death mask. Stone found that the amativeness organ of his brain was larger than average showing a large ability to love. His benevolence organ was larger than average showing an ability to be kind and yet his destructiveness organ, which displays the instinct to kill, was smaller than average.

3 – An as yet un-accessioned note in the Anatomical museum archive has written on the reverse of an image of Hare, 'Cast of head of William Hare, from mould taken in prison by Samuel Joseph, January and February 1829. The hair was close cropped except in front: which Hare would

---

[44] www.phrenology.mvm.ed.ac.uk

not allow to be done.'

4 – Burke's death mask shows a bald scalp.

5 - Howison's skeleton is currently housed in the same case as Burke. Howison was executed after being found guilty of murdering a woman by trying to remove her face with a spade. His legal representation attempted to plead insanity, it was one of the first cases of such a plea in Scotland. A summary of his case can be found in James Simpson's book[45]. Howison later confessed to killing seven other people.

6 - Burke and Hare are often erroneously described as grave robbers[46]. It was stated in Burke's court defence that he was a grave robber but this was thought to have been a ploy to help explain the appearance of a dead body in his room. In his confession he reiterates the fact that he never robbed graves.

7 - Bare in mind that Burke was described as an 'expert with the spade' by Professor Wilson, aka Christopher North in Blackwood's magazine March 1829, although he was referring to the more normal use of the spade and Burke's employment on the union canal as a navvy.

8 - Burke's exposure to both religions is documented in his confession.

9 – The Howison case was one of the first to plead insanity in Scotland. The case and other observations on homicidal insanity can be found in Simpson's book.

10 – Edwards (1980) suggests that Burke and Hare were not wastrels and

---

[45] Necessity of popular education as a national object with hints on the treatment of criminals, and observations on homicidal insanity by James Simpson. Adam and Charles Black 1834.
[46] Bailey, 2002. Burke and Hare – the year of the ghouls, page 9, Conaghan and Pickering, 2009. Burke and Hare. Notes Chapter 1.

dodgers but economic innovators. The idea of selling bodies for money was not a new one as Torrance and Waldie had been executed for it in 1752[47] but taking it to such an extreme was certainly new and not one that they were aware of being developed elsewhere. Gordon (2009) suggests that whilst Hare might have enjoyed the activity, Burke dealt with it as a business[48].

11 - The price quoted here for a body refers to their usual rate from Knox, that was £8 during the summer and £10 during the winter months when bodies were in more demand. They received £7 10s for Donald who is the only person they had traded at this point in the recollection.

12 – Whilst Burke is usually vague about dates he is surprisingly specific about this one. In the original confession it is simply 'early last spring 1828', whereas in the Courant confession it is '12th February 1828'. It is one of the only specific dates, the other being the anniversary of the Battle of Bannockburn.

13-This servant, Elizabeth Main, would prove crucial later on. She joined the Hare household in the summer of 1828 and was apparently aware of what was happening in the house[49]. After being named as a witness at the trial, she sold 21 of Hare's pigs and absconded. She was later found in Glasgow and was requested to provide evidence in the case against Hare.

14 - The encounter with Abigail Simpson is documented in Burke's confession. The order of the murders varies from biographer to biographer

---

[47] Torrance and Waldie were two women executed for the murder of an 8 year old boy. They had apparently promised to supply the doctors with the body of a child which had recently died under their care. The opportunity of removing the body from the coffin did not present itself so they managed to waylay another mother with some drink whilst they killed her son and supplied that body to the doctors. The full story is in the Appendix of MacGregor Page 275.
[48] Gordon, 2009. Infamous Burke and Hare; serial killers and resurrectionists of nineteenth century Edinburgh, page 4.
[49] Original Confession.

and even varies within the various confessions of Burke. There have been attempts to justify the difference in order[50]. I'm not sure more should be read into it than he simply forgot the order in which they happened.

15 - Gilmerton is now consumed within the urbanisation of Edinburgh. It is approximately 4 miles from the area of the West Port where Hare lived. In 1828 it would have been a mainly rural route.

16 - Most biographers agree that Burke was a violent man towards his wife, as well as Hare's wife, and that he allowed others to be violent towards her as well[51].

17 - The division of the spoils is taken from Burke's confession. It is possible that Burke is lying about the split of the money to give Hare the greater proportion, and therefore more of the guilt. The only document that cites a more equal split is to be found in the National Library of Scotland[52]. This is a diary, claiming to be from Burke. It contains a few well known facts about him and then lists the murders and amounts of money. It was found under a flagstone by a cholera cleaning team. It is written in a school exercise book claiming to belong to Burke. For this to be a genuine article, Burke would have needed to bring the school book over from Ireland with him in 1818. The book would have had to survive the fire which destroyed all of his other possessions. He would then have had to note down just the murders and the financial arrangements. He would then have had to have placed the book under the pavement of a house he no longer lived at as the book was found outside of Hare's house and

---

[50] Douglas, 1973. Burke and Hare: The true story, page 137/138. Bailey, 2002. Burke and Hare – the year of the ghouls, page 44. Edwards, 1980. The true story of the infamous Burke and Hare, page 85 and xvii.

[51] Leighton, 1862. The Court of Cacus, Page 74,79 and 120. Ireland, 1829. West Port Murders, page 181.

[52] Burks papers: full copy of the curious papers which were found under a flagstone at the general cleaning of the city, near Burke's house, where you have the names of those who were murdered and sold by him. Together with the prices and the sums received. 1832 F.3.a.13(48) Special Collections reading room, National Libraries of Scotland.

contained details of murders that occurred in Broggan's house. It would seem highly probable that the diary is not genuine and is one of the many items that came to light after the case as a way of people making money. The details contained in the confession may not be correct but it is safe to assume the money was split between them somehow.

18 - The paying of Mrs Hare is a clear indication that she was aware of the murders. As Hare had turned Kings Evidence he was unable to testify against his wife and the mentioning of this in the confession may well have been a way of ensuring some of the blame lay with Mrs Hare. Whether it is true or not, we shall never know.

Notes on Chapter 4 - Angel of Death

1 - In the 1820's there was an annual migration of harvest workers of 6000-8000 Irish. By the 1840's this had grown to 25,000.[53]

2 - All of the Irish militia disbanded in 1815 following the defeat of the French at Waterloo.

3 – Burke married Margaret Coleman whilst he was in the militia. It is not clear exactly when this happened or where but Margaret was from Ballina and it is thought that Burke attended the military hospital there[54]. The records for the Donegal Militia certainly indicate that a large number of the regiment made frequent visits to Ballina[55] although the reason is not stated. It's possible they met during one of his visits. It is not clear when the children arrived, whether during his service or after it.

4 - This information comes from the Courant confession. The Carron

[53] Education Scotland- Scottish history, migration and empire. Accessed May 2015 EducationScotland.gov.uk
[54] Edwards, 1980. The true story of the infamous Burke and Hare, page 18.
[55] Donegal Militia Muster Books and Pay list at National Archives, Kew WO 13/2761-2763.

ironworks were established in 1759 on the banks of the river Carron in Falkirk. The company was at the forefront of the industrial revolution in the UK and was one of the largest iron works in Europe in the 19th century. The company became insolvent in 1982 and was acquired by the Franke Corporation and rebranded as Carron Phoenix[56]. Up until 1815 Patrick Miller was a major shareholder in the Carron iron works. Joseph is always described as Joseph the miller and claimed he was connected by marriage – maybe it is just a coincidence.

5 – Hare's wife is documented as seldom without a black eye[57].

6 - It is easier to explain the murders in the reverse order with Joseph being killed before Abigail as it does seem a more natural progression. These two are left in the order Burke stated them in both of his confessions. Numerous people have tried to explain why the order varies, including arguments as to which weighed more on his conscience[58]. Bailey(2002) has a handy table of the differences[59]. We will never know the order, I'm not sure it matters.

7 - Walter Scott appears to have seen both confessions and expresses his opinion in a letter to John Stevenson written on 7th February 1829.
'Dear John, I return the paper (the Edinburgh Advertiser, in which the confession was first published). There is a slip in which Burke's confession differs from that of Hare. They give the same account of the number and the same description of the victims, but they differ in the order of time in which they were committed. Hare stated with great probability

[56] Watters, 1998. Where iron runs like water! A new history of Carron iron works 1759-1982.
[57] Buchanan, 1829. The trial of William Burke and Helen M'Dougal before the High Court of Justiciary at Edinburgh, page xiv. Knight, 2007. Burke and Hare, page 17. Bailey, 2002. Burke and Hare – the year of the ghouls, page 34.
[58] Douglas, 1973. Burke and Hare: The true story, pages 137-138. Bailey, 2002. Burke and Hare – the year of the ghouls, page 44. Edwards, 1980. The true story of the infamous Burke and Hare, page 85 and xvii.
[59] Bailey, 2002. Burke and Hare – the year of the ghouls, page 70.

that the body of Joseph, the miller, was the second sold, (that of the old pensioner being first) and, of course, he was the first man murdered. Burke, with less likelihood, asserts the first murder to have been that of a female lodger. I am apt to think Hare was right, for there was an additional motive to reconcile them to the deed in the miller's case – the fear that the apprehensions entertained through the fever would discredit (the house) and the consideration that there was, as they might (think) less harm in killing a man who was to die at any rate. It may be worth your reporter's while to know this, for it is a step in the history of the crime. It is not odd that Burke, acted upon as he seems always to (have been) by ardent spirits, and involved in a constant succession of murder, should have mislocated the two actions'[60]

An exert from the letter has found its way into a footnote in the official confession. The original letter is in the possession of Mr William Couch of Edinburgh.

Notes on Chapter 5 - Walter Scott

1 – It is suggested by Edwards[61] (1980) that Burke and Hare were actually economic innovators and Gordon seems to believe that Burke was in it for the money, whereas Hare enjoyed it.

2 - Burke and Hare were hardened drinkers. It is cited in Buchanan (1829) that 10-12 bottles of liquor entered the house a day[62]. They are cited often as drinking gills of whisky for breakfast. The current measure of spirits is a 1/6 of a gill, 23.7mls. A gill of whisky would be 142.2ml, or 1/4 of a pint. Although several drinks are referenced; rum and bitters and porter, their main drink would have been whisky. In some biographies this is spelt whiskey. This spelling indicates a drink from Ireland,

---

[60] Roughead, 1948. Burke and Hare. Appendix 1.
[61] Edwards, 1980. The true story of the infamous Burke and Hare, page 78.
[62] Conversation with John Gray, Buchanan, 1829. The trial of William Burke and Helen M'Dougal before the High Court of Justiciary at Edinburgh. Appendix to Trial page 59.

and whilst Burke and Hare were Irish, their drink would almost certainly have been Scottish.

3 - This phrase occurs in the Courant confession and is one of the sentences that Edwards (1980) and Conaghan (2009) suggest is out of character with the rest of the confession and puts its origins into dispute. The phrase 'they might as well be hanged for a sheep as a lamb' compliments an earlier comment about leading one of the victims in 'as a dumb lamb to the slaughter and a sheep to the shearers.' When the confession is read as a whole these two phrases do stand out but may be explained by the amount of biblical reading that Burke had been doing at the time.

4 - There was a belief at the time that there were many more victims[63]. We will never know. The victims in this story are confined to those mentioned in the confessions. Some authors have created more victims[64]. Whilst it is difficult to project morals onto Burke's character one has to wonder why he confessed to 16 if there were more. What is the difference between confessing to 16 or 20. In one transcript[65] there appears to be an interview in his cell, with a reporter from the Caledonian Mercury where he is challenged to the fact that there were actually 30 murders - his reply...' Not so many.'

Given that Burke and Hare do not seem to have had time to concoct a story, and Hare turns against him and confesses, would Hare not have told the authorities about all the murders if there had been more. Sir Walter Scott states that 'they give the same account of the number and the same description of the victims.'[66] This resemblance between the confessions would be remarkable if it were not based on the truth. The fact that the confessions were similar is also referenced in the note to the Lord Provost that prefaces the original confession.

---

[63] Interview for Caledonian Mercury January 1829 found in MacGregor, 1884. The history of Burke and Hare and of the resurrectionists times.

[64] Bryd, 1974. Rest without peace.

[65] MacGregor Page 279.

[66] Chapter 4 note 7 in this volume.

5 – This murder varies between the two Burke confessions. In the first confession there is a suggestion that this lodger was murdered by Burke alone. ' In May 1828, as he thinks, an old woman came to the house as a lodger, and she was the worse for drink, and she got more drink of her own accord, and she became very drunk, and declarant suffocated her; and Hare was not in the house at the time.'[67]

The later victim that it is thought Burke killed on his own is still mentioned in the original confession so he cannot be confusing the two occasions.

By the Courant confession the murder is performed by Hare. 'The next was an old woman who lodged with Hare for one night but does not know her name. She was murdered in the same way as above. Sold to Dr Knox for £10. The old woman was decoyed into the house by Mrs Hare in the forenoon from the street when Hare was working at the boats at the canal. She gave her whisky, and put her to bed three times. At last she was so drunk that she fell asleep; and when Hare came home to his dinner, he put part of the bed-tick on her mouth and nose, and when he came home at night she was dead.'[68]

This is a remarkable change of tune. In this story I have used the latter version of events as this is being written from Burke's point of view and he clearly wanted to push as much of the blame as possible onto the Hares.

---

[67] Original Confession.
[68] Courant Confession.

Notes on Chapter 6 – Women

1 – When Burke first appeared in the museum all of the visiting medics would have been men. The first women entered the medical school in 1869, known as the Edinburgh Seven, they were the first women to study medicine in the UK, led by Sophia Jex-Blake, who is recognised today in the naming of some University facilities. Today there are more women than men in the current student body of the medical school of the University of Edinburgh, although visitors to the museum are not exclusively from this group. In 2014/15 there were 1002 females and 682 males within the visiting student body[69].

2 – Edwards (1980) suggests that Burke's first marriage was due to a pregnancy[70]. There is no documented evidence for this. It predates the requirement for the birth to be recorded and there is an issue with Irish historical records. See note Chapter 2 note 4.
It is not clear whether Burke's children were born before he returned from the militia or not. It is also not known whether his wife moved with the militia or stayed at home with her family.

3 - This is conjecture. We know from Burke that he had at least two children in Ireland.[71] We have a variety of statements as to how long they survived. Edwards (1980) suggests that the presence of a young child may explain why his wife did not accompany Burke to Scotland. Extensive research has not identified any direct heirs of Burke. See note Chapter 2 note 4.

4 - Following his time in the militia some speculate that Burke was not unfamiliar with female casual acquaintances[72]. Edwards also suggests that his later medical problems may have started in the militia where he

---

[69] Figures from the University of Edinburgh – personal communication.
[70] Edwards, 1980. The true story of the infamous Burke and Hare, page 55.
[71] Courant Confession.
[72] Edwards, 1980. The true story of the infamous Burke and Hare, page 55.

was in and out of hospital. Edwards (1980) and others speculate it may have been syphilis[73]. The skeleton in the anatomical museum shows no signs of an advanced syphilitic infection.

5 - Burke states he was excommunicated[74]. This is a penalty of the Catholic Church which is meant to offer a way back to the church if the sinner changes their ways. Whilst a record is kept of those people excommunicated by the Pope it appears that the penalty can be applied and rescinded by local parish priests and local records from that period are not available. If Burke was excommunicated then it was probably applied by this local priest and could have been rescinded by those who attended him in the condemned cell.

6 - There is a general underlying theme to many biographies that Burke was not completely faithful[75]. We have the documented story of the younger woman whilst in Browns Close[76] and we have the case of the Mary Paterson murder, both discussed later in this chapter. It is often portrayed that most of the murder victims were prostitutes although there is little evidence for this and even less evidence that Burke associated with people of that profession.

7 – This story is told in Leighton's Court of Cacus. He portrays the police as arriving on the scene to check that Nellie was Burke's wife before he continues to beat her. He also has Nellie lying on the ground apparently

---

[73] Edwards, 1980. The true story of the infamous Burke and Hare, page 55. Leighton, 1861. The Court of Cacus, page 72.

[74] MacGregor, 1884. The history of Burke and Hare and of the resurrectionist times. Leighton, 1861. The Court of Cacus. page 72. Edwards, 1980. The true story of the infamous Burke and Hare, page 66. Ireland, 1829. West Port Murders, page 175.

[75] Leighton, 1861. The Court of Cacus, page 72. Douglas, 1973. Burke and Hare: The true story, page 28. Edwards, 1980. The true story of the infamous Burke and Hare, page 91. Ireland, 1829. West Port Murders, page 175.

[76] Leighton, 1861. The Court of Cacus, page 7. Ireland, 1829. West port Murders, page 181. MacGregor, 1884. The history of Burke and Hare and of the resurrectionist times, page 50.

dead. When she moans, Burke exclaims that there is life in her yet and continues to beat her.

8 - There is no end to this story documented. This outcome is pure conjecture to move the story along.

9 - Burke's main claim to haunting images comes from a murder not yet mentioned. I chose to have his conscience tortured from an earlier stage in the faint belief that he may have had one.

10 - Swans and Swanstons were two public houses in the area. When the story broke in 1828 the witness for this encounter, Janet Brown, placed the meeting at Swanstons[77]. Swanston took legal action against the author, Thomas Ireland, claiming that Burke had never been in his public house[78]. Ireland claimed that he had it on the best authority, the witness, that it did occur in Swanstons although the same witness apparently had trouble retracing her steps that day to try and find her friend. The case was never resolved. In the minute book of the court that holds the original list of witness[79] there are hand written notes beside each witness detailing elements of their testimony. Beside Janet Brown it clearly states Swanstons. The possibility that the location was incorrect is included here for completeness.

11 - Some biographers claim that Burke was already acquainted with these women[80], which seems unlikely considering that they took some persuading to accompany him. Earlier accounts claim he had never seen them before[81].

---

[77] Ireland, 1829. West Port Murders.

[78] Douglas, 1973. Burke and Hare: The true story, page 101. Roughead, 1948. Burke and Hare, page 24.

[79] Printed indictment and list of witnesses AD2/1/3. Court minute books JC 4/18 JC 8/23. National Records of Scotland.

[80] Knight, 2007. Burke and Hare, page 37. Buchanan, 1829. The trial of William Burke and Helen M'Dougal before the High Court of Justiciary at Edinburgh, page vii.

[81] Leighton, 1861. The Court of Cacus, page 124. MacGregor, 1884. The history of Burke and Hare and of the resurrectionist times, page 64.

12 - Mary Paterson is portrayed as a prostitute in almost all texts although her friend, Janet Brown, complained bitterly at the time that she was portrayed as such.[82]

Lisa Rosner (2010) offers a much more attractive explanation as to Mary's origins. The Magdalene Asylum used to be on the Canongate and it acted as a home for wayward girls, maids seduced by the household men or women who found themselves in need of accommodation and who had a skill such as sewing or washing that they could trade. Edinburgh City Archives contain the minute book of the Magdalene Asylum and they show a Mary Paterson entering the institute on September 18th 1826. She is the daughter of Pater Paterson, Mason. This fits with the claim in Leighton's The Court of Cacus (1861) that her mother was dead, but is at odds with the claims of Knight (2007) that she was orphaned. She had been in the service of Mr Deuchar, an engraver. This Mary Paterson appears again in the minute book on April 7th 1828 when she requests to leave the asylum. She is permitted to leave and is released onto the Canongate, the same month as the murder takes place. Could this be the same Mary Paterson? Her time in the asylum and subsequent abstinence from alcohol would explain the fact that she is portrayed in every Burke and Hare story as being unconscious from drink very quickly.

13 – This night in the cells is depicted in all texts as being Canongate Police Station. Enquires at Edinburgh City Archive suggest this was probably Canongate Tolbooth. The records for this time exist but there is no entry for Mary Paterson or Janet Brown. If they were housed for their own protection, as opposed to being charged with something, this would explain this omission. Obviously there are numerous other explanations. Rosner (2010) also found no Paterson in any police records[83] casting doubt on the claim that she was a prostitute.

14 – The attention to Janet rather than Mary is suggested in Leighton's

---

[82] Leighton, 1861. The Court of Cacus, page 131. Douglas, 1972. Burke and Hare: The true story, page 103.

[83] Rosner, 2010. The Anatomy Murders, page 116.

(1861) Court of Cacus[84] where it attributes the comment to Janet herself. 'All this attention, as Brown subsequently stated was, as she thought, directed to her in preference to Mary.'

15 – The argument that murder was maybe not the first thing on Burke's mind that morning was suggested by Knight (2007) where she states that 'Lust had temporary ascendancy over his desire to murder.'[85] I'm not sure how we can possibly know as Burke himself was silent on the matter and we only have Janet's comments on which to base any assumptions.

16 – Constantine was Burke's older brother. Burke followed him in to the Donegal militia where Constantine was an NCO. We do not know whether the two brothers came to Edinburgh together or not. Constantine is portrayed in all Burke and Hare stories as having two sons. They feature as recipients of some clothes from one of the victims and are listed as potential witness in the court case[86].

In the research undertaken to identify descendants a daughter of Constantine has been discovered. She would have been around 6-7 at the time of the crimes and probably in another house acting as a domestic help. We can be fairly certain that this person is a daughter of the family as Constantine was not a common name at this time and the mothers name is also present on the immigration papers from when the daughter went to New South Wales in 1841[87] (Fig 1 Page 145). She states her home town as Tyrone in Ireland, the original birthplace of her father, suggesting that the family returned to its origins when it left Edinburgh after the court case. Constantine was paid by the Sheriff to leave Edinburgh.[88]

17 - There has been speculation as to how much Constantine knew about his brother's business. He was stopped in the street by Janet Brown dur-

---

[84] Leighton, 1861. The Court of Cacus, page 124.

[85] Knight, 2007. Burke and Hare, page 39.

[86] Trial listing National Records of Scotland. AD 2/1/3.

[87] Rupparti@gmail.com

[88] MacGregor, 1884. The history of Burke and Hare and of the resurrectionist times, page 167.

ing 1828 and always responded by saying 'How the hell can I tell about you sort of people. You are here today and away tomorrow. I am often out upon my lawful business, how can I answer for all that takes place in my house in my absence.'[89]

He was never implicated by Burke although he did have to leave town after the court case so clearly the general public thought he was involved in some manner.

18 – This is possibly because of her years of abstinence in the Magdalene Asylum although there is another possible explanation – see note 23

19 - In Janet Brown's later statement, which never made it to court, she claimed 'However much she might have been disposed to yield to his wishes…'[90] This is then referenced in a statement in Leighton's The Court of Cacus that 'she would have laid with him."

The implication in both statements is that Burke had attempted to persuade her to do more than just join him for a drink. Whether this was simply as a means to murder her or more, we will never know. Burke is silent on it in his confession.

Whilst there is speculation as to the motives for Burke and Hare and the suggestion that it may have had sexual motives, some even going as far as to suggest necrophilia,[91] given the lack of any evidence I choose to believe that their motives were financial and nothing more.

20 – Roughead (1948) writes that 'Nellie was determined to restrict his relations with them to 'that' act alone.'[92] This reinforces the idea that Burke may have been thinking about more than simply murdering these girls, and his wife knew it.

21 – Edwards (1980) suggests that Burke's original name had been Liam

---

[89] Leighton, 1861. The Court of Cacus, page 131.
[90] Ireland, 1829. West Port Murders, page 128.
[91] Bryd, 1974. Rest without peace, page 135.
[92] Roughead, 1948. Burke and Hare, page 26.

D'Burca. There does not appear to be any evidence to support this. As mentioned in note 16, Constantine appears to have returned to Ireland after the court case. If he had changed his name to fit in when he went to Scotland, would there not be some argument to change it back when he returned to Ireland? It is stated on his daughter's immigration papers as Burke.

22 – Constantine is reported in the Courant as having once taken a chest to Surgeons' Square for Burke. He was paid 10 shillings but refused to do it again.[93]

23 – Much is made of the fact that Mary Paterson was a prostitute and at least one of the students had been with her a few nights previously. Given Janet Brown's objection to the portrayal of her friend is it not more likely that the Doctors knew Mary Paterson from a possible encounter in the hospital?

If we accept Rosner's (2010) suggestion that Mary Paterson was an inmate of the Magdalene Asylum than had she been ill she would have been treated at the Royal Infirmary. A Mary Paterson was in the hospital in March 1828 and would have been seen by a doctor. This also offers an explanation for the other name that is ascribed to this victim, Mary Mitchell. Both women were in the hospital, on the same ward and may have been seen by the same doctor. Mary Mitchell died, whilst Mary Paterson recovered. Of the doctors who were rostered on the ward at the time, none were assistants of Knox's but a swap of shifts would not be recorded and maybe offers a more reasonable explanation than the more popular prostitute story. If we add to this the fact that hospital records show that Mary Paterson was in the hospital for a liver complaint[94] then we also have another possible explanation as to why the drink affected her so quickly. The records show that she was released on the 11th of April 1828. This means, if it is the same Mary Paterson, that she would

---

[93] MacGregor, 1884. The history of Burke and Hare and of the resurrectionist times, page 167.
[94] Lothian health board records, personal communication.

have been released from the asylum whilst she was actually in hospital. This is not an impossible situation as a request to leave would have been submitted prior to the committee meeting. It does mean that a doctor would have seen her and declared her fit only a few days before she appeared dead at Dr Knox's. In Lonsdale (1870) it simply states that 'a pupil of Knox's, who had been in her company only a few nights previously.'[95] It does not say in what capacity.

24 – Many of the pictures portraying Mary Paterson are very artistic. The original one painted by John Oliphant for Knox shows her in a semi-erotic pose reminiscent of the Rokeby Venus of Velazquez[96]. An original student drawing exists in the National Library of Scotland which portrays a much simpler picture of a woman, lying on her side, drawn from behind. (See Figure 2 Page 146.)

[95] Lonsdale, 1870. A sketch of the life and writings of Robert Knox the anatomist, page 101.
[96] Kaufman, 1997.

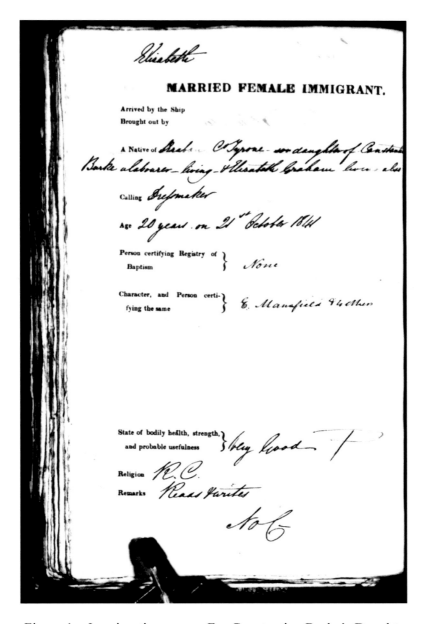

Figure 1 – Immigration papers For Constantine Burke's Daughter

Figure 2 – The two representations of Mary Paterson

This drawing shows how the way the body was represented by
the artist, John Oliphant, brought in by Knox

This drawing shows how the body is represented by a medical
student at the time. Original in NLS

Notes on Chapter 7 – Inappropriate Behaviour

1 - Prior to 1872 the main method of death by hanging in the UK was strangulation. The development of a system that allowed for a longer drop and dislocated the neck was first suggested in an article in 1866[97]. Following the adoption of this method hanging now kills by three methods, dislocation of the neck, internal rupture of the jugular vein and strangulation[98]. Burke was executed in 1829 and therefore the plan would have been to strangle him.

2 –According to Leighton (1861) parts of Burke's skin were made into a tobacco duct and a picture backing[99]. A pocket book is currently on display at the Royal College of Surgeons', although the authenticity of this is debated by some. They do have papers accounting for its providence[100]. A calling card case is at the Caddies office in the Grassmarket. This has been confirmed as being made of human skin and can be traced back to the time of the dissection[101], Figure 3 pages 148-149. In the Court of Cacus a tale is told of another section of the skin being removed, tanned and then decorated with images. This is reported as being in the procession of Mr Fraser, a jeweller and collector of antiquities[102] Gordon (2007) reports that during the dissection pieces of skin were stolen and appeared as souvenirs[103]. A section of skin has recently been found in Stirling with documentation tracing it back to the time[104].

---

[97] On Hanging, considered from a Mechanical and Physiological point of view", in The London, Edinburgh and Dublin Philosophical Magazine and Journal of Science, vol. xxxii, of, 1866.

[98] Duff, 1954. A new handbook on hanging; being a short introduction to the fine art of execution, containing much useful information on neck-breaking, throttling, strangling, asphyxiation, decapitation and electrocution.

[99] Leighton,1861. The Court of Cacus, note 18 page 235.

[100] Conanghan, 2009. Burke and Hare, Chapter 13 notes and personal communication with the Royal College of Surgeons of Edinburgh.

[101] Personal communication.

[102] Leighton, 1861. The Court of Cacus, page 235.

[103] Gordon,2009. Infamous Burke and Hare: serial killers and resurrectionists of nineteenth century Edinburgh, page 177.

[104] Personal communication.

After the trial various bits of the Hare's house were sold off, although Burke's house was not exploited to the same extent[105]. When the West Port area was demolished in the early 1900's various items came on the market claiming to be made from the timbers of the house in Tanners' close. Fig 4 page 150.

Figure 3 – Artefacts made from Burkes skin.

The calling card case reportedly made from Burke's skin currently held by the Cadies and Witchery tours in Edinburgh. *Reproduced by kind permission of The Cadies and Witchery Tours.*

---

[105] Ireland 1829 Page 109.

Section of Skin and Documentation in Stirling *Reproduced by kind permission of Smith Art Gallery and Museum.*

The note book reportedly bound in Burke's skin currently held by the Surgeons' Hall Museum in Edinburgh. *Reproduced by kind permission of Surgeons' Hall Museum.*

Figure 4 – Artefacts from the house

A Snuff box apparently made from the timbers of Tanners' Close.
Reproduced by kind permission of James Peacock, Joppa.

3 – Alexander Monro 'tertius' did exactly this. "This is written in the blood of William Burke, he was hanged at Edinburgh on 28th January 1829 for the murder of Mrs Campbell or Docherty. The blood was taken from his head on the 1st of Feb
1829" is preserved on a piece of paper held in the Centre for Research Collections at the University of Edinburgh. (Figure 5 Page 154.)

4 – It is for precisely this reason that David Boyle, Lord Justice Clerk, suggested the skeleton should be preserved. See Page 108.

5- In the copy of Christison's book – A treatise on Poisons, held by the Royal Medical Society in Edinburgh, there is a handwritten note on page 530.
Edwards attributes this note to Christison himself, claiming it is a note made after an interview in the prison cell[106].It is impossible to confirm who wrote this note or when. The note reads:-
'Burke / the murderer / took an ounce and a half when drunk without any bad effect.'

---

[106] Edwards, 1980. The true story of the infamous Burke and Hare, page xiii.

It is made beside a paragraph discussing the effect of opiates whilst drunk stating that Mr Shearman related a story of a habitual drunkard who, whilst intoxicated, took 2 ounces of laudanum and had no ill effect for 5 hours, at which point he died of opium poisoning.

From this note it would appear that someone discovered that Burke took opiates. They were either told by someone who was very close to him, told by Burke himself, fabricated the fact or they were experimenting on him in prison.

If Burke could withstand an ounce and a half with no ill effect and yet two ounces can kill a man then it may be possible that he was a regular user who had built up a tolerance to the drug. Maybe a percentage of his income was being spent on a developing drug reliance.

6 – In The Court of Cacus, it is the Hare's that bring in these victims.[107]

7 – Physical violence between the culprits has been referenced earlier, Chapter 3 note 16.

8 – This is an estimate of the date. In the whole of Burke's confession there are only 3 exact dates, the first murder, the last murder, and the anniversary of the Battle of Bannockburn.

9 – The court case only looked at the circumstances around the last murder but Mrs Hare stated 'She had seen such tricks before.'[108] Some biographers have her much more involved with the crimes.

10 – This was not uncommon practice at the time.

11 – The first story to claim that the child's back was broken was Ireland's[109] (1829), Leighton (1876) went a stage further stating Burke said

[107] Leighton, 1876. The Court of Cacus, page 104.
[108] Buchanan, 1829. The trial of William Burke and Helen M'Dougal before the High Court of Justiciary at Edinburgh.
[109] Ireland, 1829. West Port Murders, page 193.

so himself 'as he himself expressed it.'[110] The whole 'broken back' argument is detailed in Edwards (1980)[111], accompanied by his opinion that no story of Burke and Hare is complete without an analysis of the incident. Edwards claims the original story came from Ireland's retelling[112], who was in the business of selling his pamphlets at the time. Adams (1972), Douglas (1973) and Leighton (1829) then repeat Ireland's story[113]. Knight (2007), along with later writers, concedes that it is far more likely that the boy was smothered. Whilst Conaghan and Pickering (2009) leave the incident out of their graphic novel because of the controversy, they do picture the boy's face in a nightmare scene[114]. The incident does not appear in any of the confessions. These simply state that the boy was killed in the same way as the others. Whilst this phrase may well be shorthand of the transcriber surely such a deviation from their original method would have been mentioned. Although Burke was described as a muscular man, the effort involved in breaking the back of a child by hugging them would be immense and why go to that trouble when you have developed a system that works so well. I believe the child was smothered and hence that is how it is represented here.

12 – The final victim did show some separation of the ligaments in the neck area.[115] The spinal column was intact and the force exerted on the neck was used to get the body into the chest. The results of the post mortum examination are mentioned in the court papers.

13 – The study of anatomy suffered from insufficient supply of cadaveric material. The Anatomy Act was passed in 1832 to address this problem.

---

[110] Leighton, 1876. The Court of Cacus, page 108.
[111] Edwards, 1980. The true story of the infamous Burke and Hare, pages 92-99.
[112] Edwards, 1980. The true story of the infamous Burke and Hare, page 95.
[113] Adams, 1972. Dead and buried: The horrible history of bodysnatching, pages 88 and 9. Douglas, 1973. Burke and Hare:The true story, page 46. Leighton, 1876. The Court of Cacus, page 108.
[114] Conaghan, 2009. Burke and Hare, chapter 4 pages 16-17.
[115] Buchanan, 1829. The trial of William Burke and Helen M'Dougal before the High Court of Justiciary at Edinburgh, page 121. Ireland, 1829. West Port Murders and Roughead, 1948. Burke and Hare.

Prior to the Act the legal supply was limited to executed criminals, whilst illegal supply drove people to grave robbing and murder. Whilst Burke and Hare are often credited with forcing the passing of the Anatomy Act, which did not have a smooth ride through parliament, it was actually agreed after the execution of John Bishop and Thomas Williams, the London Burkers in 1831. Bishop and Thomas drugged their victims with laudanum and then drowned them so the only similarity was that they attempted to sell their victim to a medical school. Full details of the case and the passage of the Anatomy Act can be found in MacGregor (1884)[116]. Although much is made of the supply of bodies from Burke and Hare it should be noted that they only supplied Knox with less than 10% of his annual usage[117].

---

[116] MacGregor, 1884. The history of Burke and Hare and of the resurrectionist times, page 258 onwards.

[117] Talk at Edinburgh University by Prof. Gordon Findlater. Figures for cadavers usage in 1820's Edinburgh. Knox 247, Lizars 138, Monro 88, Aitken 47. A more conservative estimate of 90 bodies a year is given in Wormersley and Crawford, 2010.

Figure 5 – The original letter written by Monro in Burke's blood.

Reproduced by kind permission of Edinburgh University Library.

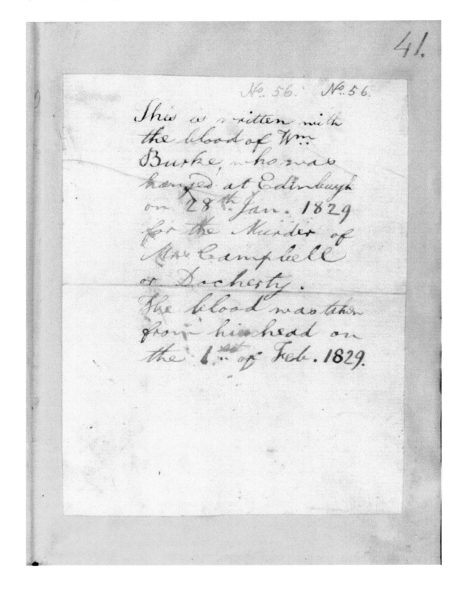

Notes on Chapter 8 – Highs and Lows

1 – The Scottish Judicial System has a jury of 15 rather than the 14 preferred by the English system. This is to stop the possibility of a hung jury.[118]

2 – 'Meant to be fed on bread and water.' There are three separate accounts, one in the London Standard 26th Jan 1829[119], one in the Caledonian Mercury paper of the time[120], and one is also found in Ireland (1829)[121] stating that Burke's diet was changed on medical grounds.

3 – Murder Act 1751 section XI states 'provided always, and it is hereby enacted by the authority aforesaid, that nothing herein contained shall extend to repeal or alter so much of an act made in the eleventh year of his late Majesty's reign (intitled, An Act for the more effectual disarming the Highlands in that part of Great Britain called Scotland; and for the better securing the peace and quiet of that part of the kingdom) as relates to the suspension of the execution of persons convicted of capital offences within that part of Great Britain called Scotland, for the respective times in the said mentioned; anything herein before contained to the contrary notwithstanding.'[122] The timing of 30 and 40 days are stated in the 1725 act mentioned above.

4 – The full Wilson case can be found in Robert Buchanan (2) (1829) and George MacGregor (1884), listed in the bibliography.

5 – The fact that Hare had turned Kings Evidence and a private case was then taken out against him caused much judicial pondering. In the end the Judges decided that there could not be a private criminal case against

---

[118] Duff, 1999. The Scottish criminal jury: a very peculiar institution.
[119] Available in the National Library of Scotland Burke and Hare material.
[120] Available in the National Library of Scotland Burke and Hare material.
[121] Ireland, 1829. West Port Murders, page 211.
[122] The Murder Act of 1751 – Wikisource, the free online library.

him for the murder of James Wilson as he had given that evidence believing that it could not be used in court. If the case was allowed to proceed then what would stop Docherty's relatives attempting to prosecute him for the murder that was actually covered in the court case and for which he was definitely protected.[123] The Wilson's proceeded with a civil case to cover the financial loss to the family due to the death of Jamie. As Hare had no money he was to stay in jail until he could pay the £500. As this was never going to happen, the Wilson's dropped their case and he was freed on the 5th of February 1829.[124]

6 – The inside of the barrel refers to the barrel that the body was packed away in after the dissection according to Leighton (1861) and Roughead (1948).[125] Other biographers have the skeleton being prepared straight away.[126] The skeleton was also packed away during the war to protect it from bomb damage.[127]

7 – Edinburgh's Anatomical Museum, founded and developed by the Monro Dynasty, flourished under Sir William Turner, Professor of Anatomy 1867-1903, and thereafter principle of the University till his death in 1917. Turner's main interests were in comparative mammalian anatomy, anthropology and craniology and Edinburgh was unusual in that these aspects remained firmly based in the medical faculty. The Anatomical Museum was the central feature of Rowand Anderson's Medical School, designed as a three-storey top lit galleried hall, with skeletons of whales and dolphins suspended from the ceiling and a wealth of specimens on display. In the 1950's the hall was subdivided into three separate storeys

[123] Bailey, 2002. Burke and Hare – the year of the ghouls, page 127.
[124] The whole case against Hare can be found in MacGregor, 1884. The history of Burke and Hare and of the resurrectionist times, page 183.
[125] Leighton, 1861. The Court of Cacus, page 235, Roughead, 1948. Burke and Hare, page 66.
[126] Knight, 2007. Burke and Hare, page 95. Bailey, 2002. Burke and Hare – the year of the ghouls, page 118.
[127] Edinburgh Evening News 1st August 1942.

and many of the non-human specimens were transferred to other institutions. The whales went to the Royal Scottish Museum, now the National Museums Scotland. The imposing museum lobby at Teviot Place, University of Edinburgh, still contains the elephant skeletons.

8 – The view of the museum is shown in Fig 6 Page 161. This is based on drawings of the museum that show where Burke's skeleton was located when the museum was in its original three storey condition.

9 - The skeleton of Burke featured in the closing credits of the Simon Pegg's Burke and Hare film. It was relocated to the lobby of the museum for filming the final scene.

10 – The flayed man sculpture is entitled 'From Nature' and was allegedly cast from an anatomical specimen prepared by John Goodsir who studied anatomy under Knox. Goodsir was a demonstrator at the University in 1844 and became the Curator of the Anatomical Museum in 1845. The sculpture bears a plate engraved with the date 1845.

11 – The elephants are currently on the first floor flanking the doorway to the Anatomical Museum.

12 – There are also claims that Andrew Williamson was a neighbour of Burkes although he does not appear in the floor plan of the house.[128]

13 – Burke's skeleton indicates that he was 5'4" tall although it may not be 100% accurate as it has obviously been rearticulated.

14 – Burke is quoted in an interview as saying he 'had a good character with the police; or if they had known that there were four murderers living in one house they would have visited more oftener.'[129] Notice he says

---

[128] Douglas, 1973. Burke and Hare: The true story, page 44.
[129] McGregor, 1884. The history of Burke and Hare and of the resurrectionist times.

'4 murderers' – how innocent were the others?

15 – There is one comment that is in opposition to this statement. 'The Echo of Surgeons' Square', written after the case in 1829, states that 'suspicion fell on Burke October last – a policeman was stationed at his door.' We have to consider that this story is not corroborated by any other writer and the author of the Echo is unclear. Many believe it to be David Paterson, Knox's assistant who, at the time of publication, had been sacked by Knox and left to take much of the blame. Bailey (2002) disagrees[130] pointing out that the style is unlikely to have been composed by someone of Paterson's standing. The Caledonian mercury of the time (17th January 1829) published a letter from David Paterson in which he states, 'it is my wish to give the public every information that lies in my power, which will shortly be done by another individual who is more capable than I am.'

16 – There is much debate as to what this old injury was. There seems to be unanimous agreement that there was something wrong with Burke's testicles. Bailey (2002) points out that considering the horrendous crimes that Burke committed it is somewhat ironic that his testicles are still considered taboo. Most people come down in favour of testicular cancer, unfortunately this is impossible to prove as it would not be detectable even if we had his entire DNA sequence from the skeleton. Edwards (1980) points out that Burke was in and out of hospital during his militia days and that this affliction might have started then.[131] This information come from the Donegal Militia material at the National Archives in Kew where they only actually record two visits to hospital in the three years that the records cover.[132] These were in April – May 1809 to the Regimental Hospital and then October-November of the same year to the General Hospital in Dublin. Unfortunately records no longer exist to allow us to know what these admissions were for.

[130] Bailey, 2002. Burke and Hare – the year of the ghouls, page 141.
[131] Edwards,1980. The true story of the infamous Burke and Hare, page 18.
[132] WO 13/2761-2765 National Archives at Kew.

There are frequent references to a scirrhous testicle – a scirrhous carcinoma being a hard slow growing malignant tumour.[133] Bryd (1974) claims to have seen a Latin medical report that states Burke could have been suffering from tubercular ulceration, syphilis or cancer[134]. Edwards (1980) also mentions the possibility of syphilis [135] although the skeleton in the anatomical museum shows no signs of an advanced syphilitic infection. Douglas (1973)[136] and the Echo of Surgeons' Hall both claim that Burke had his wound dressed by Knox. The Echo even adding that he returned when it took on a more dangerous appearance. It must be remembered that the Echo was written to highlight Knox's involvement in the case and it would certainly be hard to deny any knowledge of someone if you were dressing such an intimate wound. Knight (2007) [137] claims documented evidence of testicular cancer citing Atlay (1899) 'Famous trials of the century'. Atlay (1899) does not confirm testicular cancer but suggests that surgery was performed in the condemned cell.[138] This seems highly unlikely given the survival rate for surgery at that time and the likelihood of a riot if they had managed to kill Burke before his public execution.

A number of references are made to the fact that the public believed the illness to be related to Jamie's murder – 'Burke threw himself across Jamie's legs – sustaining a painful injury to his testicles.'[139]

'a cancerous affection from saliva of a bite from Jamie was believed but… it was a peculiar external malady with which he had for a considerable time been afflicted.'[140]

'He told the minister of the Tolbooth Church, who was attending on him,

---

[133] Edwards, 1980. The true story of the infamous Burke and Hare, page 55. Knight, 2007. Burke and Hare, page 90. Douglas, 1973. Burke and Hare: The true story, page 53.
[134] Bryd, 1974. Rest without peace, page 202.
[135] Edwards1980. The true story of the infamous Burke and Hare, page 55.
[136] Douglas, 1973. Burke and Hare: The true story, page 111.
[137] Knight, 2007. Burke and Hare, page 80.
[138] Atlay, 1899. Famous trials of the century, page 42.
[139] Knight,2007. Burke and Hare, page 53.
[140] Leighton, 1861. The Court of Cacus, note 15 Page 234.

that it arose from a bite given by 'Daft Jamie' when he was being done to death'[141]

Bryd has frequent references to his inability to have sex without pain and bleeding.

The Latin medical report has been found, buried deep in the pages of Thomas Stone's phrenology paper. Having had it translated[142] and having consulted with University of Edinburgh pathologists and experts in this area[143], it is safe to rule out the possibility that he was suffering from testicular cancer. It is more likely that he was suffering from a selection of sexually transmitted diseases. These could have included secondary syphilis, accounting for the lack of bone deformation which occurs with tertiary syphilis. This syphilitic infection could have caused epididymo-orcthitis which would have accounted for some of the described symptoms. Chlamydia may account for some of the signs with rarer older diseases of the day such as lymphogranuloma venerum and granuloma inguinale possibly accounting for the infection and cutaneous symptoms listed in the medical report.

Whatever the truth is it seems highly probable that there was something wrong with Burke. It was probably to do with his testicles and it was bad enough that his diet was changed from bread and water in his final month[144]. It seems safe to conclude he probably wasn't entertaining a lot of women.

---

[141] Atlay, 1899. Famous trials of the century, page 42.

[142] Page 208 of this volume

[143] Translated by Felicity Loughlin and consulted with Prof. Lee Smith and Dr. Tim Kendall.

[144] Newspaper report in NLS from London Standard 26th January 1829.

Figure 6 – Burke's view of the Museum

Notes on Chapter 9 – Bannockburn

1 – The Battle of Bannockburn was a two day battle which took place on the 23-24th June 1314 at Bannockburn, south of Stirling. The English were led by Edward II and the Scots were led by Robert the Bruce. The Scots won.

2 - Up until his conviction, Burke maintained that Helen M'Dougal knew nothing about their murderous activities. She was never described as being a particularly smart woman but she would have had to have been very slow to not have suspicions as to what was occurring.

In his prayers before execution, Burke is reported to have prayed for Helen and that she find a way out of the evil that he has introduced her to. This seems to imply she was maybe not completely unaware. There is also his earlier noted comment about there being 4 murderers in the house. Chapter 8 note 14.

3 – Both stories are reported in numerous retellings of the case.[145]

4 – Beatings and infidelity have been referenced in Chapter 3 note 16 and Chapter 6 note 6 respectively.

5 – All histories make mention of this fire and for some reason state the four books that were on the shelf. Looking unto Jesus by Ambrose, Fourfold State by Boston, Pilgrims Progress by Bunyan and Reign of Grace by Booths.[146] These books must have belonged to Burke as M'Dougal was illiterate, as declared in the court proceedings. How anyone knows which books were on a shelf that was totally consumed by fire is never explained.

---

[145] Ireland, 1829. West Port Murders, page 188. Leighton, 1861. The Court of Cacus, page 96. Douglas, 1973. Burke and Hare: The true story, page 38.

[146] Edwards, 1980. The true story of the infamous Burke and Hare, page 66. Leighton, 1861. The Court of Cacus, page 72.

6 – John Broggan was burnt as a child and so the skin around his face and neck was unusual in appearance. In addition to this he had a facial deformity that caused his lower teeth to protrude and a form of growth on his lower lip. A wax model of his face, and his actual skull, are held by Surgeons' Hall Museum, Edinburgh. The image appears in Conaghan and Pickering (2009)[147]. (Figure 7 Page 164)

7 – It was the usual practice in 1828 to sublet the room in which you still resided. This would mean that Burke and M'Dougal would have moved in to the same room as John Broggan and his heavily pregnant wife. This arrangement makes it very hard to explain how the Broggan's and M'Dougal could have been unaware of Burke's activities. It is very unlikely that Mrs Broggan would have been 'out' during later murders as claimed considering how late in her pregnancy she was. Why would Burke have gone to the effort of claiming she was out if she were not residing in the same room and hence had the possibility of being in? John Broggan was not a wealthy man, as we shall discover later, and so it is very unlikely that he had spare rooms that he let out.[148] The situation is glossed over in most accounts of the murders.

8 – Burke is depicted as moving out after the confrontation with the intention of severing his connection with Hare. It is also suggested that there was no such confrontation and the relocation to other premises was a calculated move to expand the business.[149]

---

[147] Conaghan and Pickering, 2009. Burke and Hare, page 19.
[148] Bryd, 1974. Rest without peace, page 107.
[149] Leighton, 1861. The Court of Cacus, page 135.

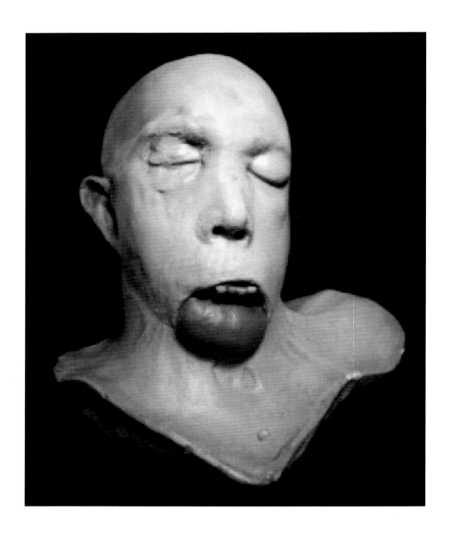

Figure 7 – The wax model of John Broggan's face at the Surgeons' Hall Museum, Edinburgh.

Reproduced by kind permission of Surgeons' Hall Museum.

Notes on Chapter 10 – Blast from the Past

1 – There are stories that Helen M'Dougal ended up in Australia, dying there in 1868 [150] and we have the immigration papers of Burke's niece who went to New South Wales. (Figure 1 Page 145.)

2 – There is much discrepancy in the Haldane story. Many biographers have her being entertained by Margaret and Nellie. Burke is silent on the details so I chose to have her never enter the house or encounter the women. He states that she was a lodger of Hare's although most people treat her as a former lodger. He states that she was killed in the stable so this is a story that conveniently places her in the correct location.

3 – Many biographers claim that the daughter was searching for her mother and was directed to Hare's house. People had remembered Burke chasing away children who had been calling Mary names as they origi-nally made their way back to the house. Mary Haldane is described by Burke as being killed in the stable.
Peggy Haldane, her daughter, was killed in Burke's house. Whilst not far from Hare's house it is not a location that her mother is reported to have been in so it is difficult to explain why she would have been there. He refers to her in one confession as Margaret and in the other as Peggy and claims he had no idea why she was in his house drunk. Bailey (2002) suggests it could have been for sex.[151] Maybe he did not want to mention that she was searching for her mother because it puts too much of a hu-man angle on to his killing spree, maybe it was a coincidence, or maybe he just couldn't come up with a believable explanation as to why he had a drunk woman in his house.

4 – It is stated in the confession that she was killed by pushing her down into the bed clothes, not in the same manner as the others. The phrase 'to

---

[150] Adams, 1972. Dead and buried: The horrible history of bodysnatching, page 86.
[151] Bailey, 2002. Burke and Hare – the year of the ghouls, page 44.

burke' has entered the English language as a means to 'supress or stifle', although it also refers to their specific method of killing by holding the nose and mouth shut. A method, that according to Burke's confessions, he never actually performed although that is contradicted by his comments to the reporter in his cell.[152]

Notes on Chapter 11 – The Path to Destruction

1 – Daft Jamie, and the stories that surround him, are mentioned in many other biographies. There are whole volumes about him that were printed many years after his death i.e. 'Laconic narrative of the life and death of James Wilson, known by the name of Daft Jamie: in which are interspersed, several anecdotes relative to him and his old friends Boby Awl, an idiot who strolled about Edinburgh for many year.' By William Smith (1881).[153]

2 – There is some debate as to how well known Jamie was before he was murdered and whether his character was created after the event by the media. It is hard to find a reference to Daft Jamie that predates the Burke and Hare case but this does not prove or disprove the suggestion.

3 – Hare's version of what happened in that room appears in the court transcript[154], and in the indictment section 2 on page 180. Burke's counter statements can be found in his third confession on page 203

4 – Jamie is described as having a club foot and his unusual anatomical appearance is described in the Echo of Surgeons' Square.

---

[152] Interview with Caledonian Mercury Journalist MacGregor,1884. The history of Burke and Hare and of resurrectionist times, page 279.

[153] Available in the Centre for Research Collection, University of Edinburgh.

[154] Buchanan, 1829. The trial of William Burke and Helen M'Dougal before the High Court of Justiciary at Edinburgh, page viii. MacGregor, 1884. The history of Burke and Hare and of the resurrectionist times, page 96.

5 – Burke was found with a snuff box and spoon but he claimed the box was his own, Jamie's having been discarded sometime before.[155]

6 – The fact that Lucky was not paid and did not speak to him for three weeks appears in the original confession as well as several version of the tale since.[156]

Notes on Chapter 12 – Two More Women

1 – As the story unfolds it is hard to picture the Broggan's living in the same room as Burke and M'Dougal and not being aware of his activities. Some claim that he was aware of everything[157]. See previous note on the Broggans – Chapter 9 note 7.

2 – King George IV visited Scotland in 1822, the first reigning monarch to do so since 1650. The event was organised by Sir Walter Scott and it was his inclusion of tartan that elevated the tartan kilt to become part of Scotland's national identity.

3 – Burke was maybe not aware of the risks that they were taking. According to some, two women come looking for Ann M'Dougal, her mother and her sister. They tracked down Constantine Burke, although it is not clear why they were looking for him, and were told by Nellie 'Oh you need not trouble yourselves about Jessy. She was murdered and sold long ago.'[158] To have an accomplice talking about their dealings in such an open way was clearly a risk and would cast doubts on her innocence if true.

---

[155] Original confession, 'Courant' confession and third confession.
[156] Roughead, 1948. Burke and Hare, page 35. Douglas, 1973. Burke and Hare :The true story, page 54.
[157] Leighton, 1861. The Court of Cacus. Douglas, 1973, Burke and Hare :The true story, page 48.
[158] Leighton, 1861. The Court of Cacus, page 119.

4 – In the confession Burke says they gave Broggan money that 'he might not come against them for the murder of Ann M'Dougal that he saw in the trunk.' Had he looked inside it? Bailey (2002) [159] suggests that they might have been stupid enough to actually leave the trunk open, or maybe it was unavoidable as he was living in the same room.

Notes of Chapter 13 – The Final Victim

1 – Direct quote from Burke in MacGregor (1884)[160].

2 –Burke never claimed his name was Docherty, he claimed it was his mother's name. As pointed out by his lawyer in court – it might have been[161]. Unfortunately we can not find his birth records to confirm this.

3 – The White Hart has been a public house in the Grassmarket area of Edinburgh since 1516. It was adjacent to the West Port area of town and Burke and Hare probably would have frequented it. A board outside the pub claims that they met many of their victims there and that one victim still haunts the premises.

4- According to the prison records Burke was 36 and Hare 21 when they were arrested.[162] Hare was also a 'sorry pugilist'[163].

5 – Who ran down the corridor would be debated in court. We shall never know as the testimonies differ. It makes more sense for it to have been Docherty at this point. The two other women would have seen Burke and Hare fight before.

---

[159] Bailey, 2002. Burke and Hare – the year of the ghouls, page 65.
[160] MacGregor, 1884. The history of Burke and Hare and of the resurrectionist times, page 100.
[161] Buchanan, 1829. The trial of William Burke and Helen M'Dougal before the High Court of Justiciary at Edinburgh, page 159.
[162] Prison Records HH21/8/1. National Records of Scotland.
[163] Leighton, 1861. The Court of Cacus, page 77.

6 – The fact that David Paterson sent his fifteen year old sister to Burke's house will be used as evidence that he could not have been aware of their line of trade.

7 – The Mob attacked Knox's house after the court case[164]. They broke all of his windows and burned him in effigy. It was reported in the papers on Tuesday 10th February 1829[165].

8 – The first police on the scene would do exactly that, until the alibis didn't match. If they had spent more time arranging their cover story we might never have known about Burke and Hare.

9 – The splitting of the money would be a great debate in court. Was the money given to Paterson who then split it between them? Did Burke give Hare his share? Who paid the porter?[166]

Notes on Chapter 14 – Court

1 – These versions of events are taken from the declarations that Burke made to the Sheriff and are present in the court transcripts.[167]

2 – Of the four prisoners M'Dougal was not talking. Burke was judged to be the ringleader due to his intellect and age, he was 36 whereas the two women were early thirties and Hare was only 21.

3 – There are many stories as to what happened to Hare. He was put onto the coach to Dumfries as Mr Black but recognised by the Wilson's lawyer. The police protected him from the mob that tried to attack him and sent him off towards the border. The traditional story is that he was

---

[164] Lonsdale, 1870. A sketch of the life and writings of Robert Knox the anatomist, page 109.

[165] Newspaper reports are available at the National Libraries of Scotland.

[166] Ireland, 1829. West Port Murders, page 87.

[167] Buchanan, 1829. The trial of William Burke and Helen M'Dougal before the High Court of Justiciary at Edinburgh, page 124 onwards.

thrown into a lime pit and died as a blind beggar on the streets on London. However, if you look through all the newspaper cuttings held by the National Library of Scotland and the University of Edinburgh Centre for Research Collections then reports can be found of a lynching in Londonderry[168], an execution in New York[169], eye witnesses in Wigton, Carlisle, Whitehaven and Belfast[170], with a confession and death in Orrey on Saturday 29th May 1841[171]. Although why he would have returned to Burke's home town, and it still be spelt wrong, are not explained.

4 – The indictment is reproduced within this volume and can be found at the National Records of Scotland.[172]

5 - Edwards (1980) suggests that Moncreiff and Cockburn were representing the accused more to discredit the Tory administration[173] then to defend their clients.

6 – The political scene in 1829 was one of reformation[174]. The Whigs were looking for opportunities to upset the current Tory administration and they frequently used the legal system and the differences between England and Scotland to do so. All of the lawyers who offered their services to Burke and M'Dougal were Whigs, arguably using the case as a way to embarrass the Tory administration for the lack of progression on the Anatomy Act. The parliamentary committee looking into the provision of material for medical schools was Whig led. Within a few years the Whigs would be in power[175].

7 - According to Atlay (1899) 'Had they been tried in England, not all

---

[168] Cited in Bailey,2002. Burke and Hare – the year of the ghouls, page 128.
[169] Published by Neil and Co in the National Library of Scotland collection.
[170] Centre for Research Collections. University of Edinburgh.
[171] National Library of Scotland RVIIIA6.
[172] Printed indictment AD 2/1/3. National Records of Scotland.
[173] Edwards, 1980. The true story of the infamous Burke and Hare, page xi.
[174] Pentland 2008. Radicalism, Reform and National identity in Scotland 1820-1833.
[175] Rosner, 2010. The Anatomy Murders, page 43.

the wealth of the Indies would at that date have rendered it possible for counsel to do more than cross examine witnesses on their behalf.'[176]

8 – Burke's legal team was led by Sir James Moncrieff who was educated at Edinburgh University. He became Solicitor General in 1850 and was then Lord Advocate on four occasions between 1851 and 1869. He served as Lord Justice Clerk from 1869-1888.

Patrick Robertson was the son of James Robertson, the writer to the signet. Patrick was educated at Edinburgh High School and called to the bar on the 27th May 1815. In November 1843 he would replace Lord Meadowbank as an ordinary Lord of Session. He died in January 1855 and a marble tablet marks his memory in St Giles' cathedral, Edinburgh. Duncan McNeill was educated at St Andrews University and would become Solicitor General of Scotland in 1834 and then Lord Advocate from 1842-46.

David Milne was the junior counsel at Burke's case and he was tasked with interviewing the prisoner, an experience that apparently affected him greatly. He gave up legal practice in 1845 to become a country gentleman[177].

9 - Henry Cockburn was educated at the Royal High School and then the University of Edinburgh. He would become Solicitor General from 1830-34. He became a Judge in the Court of Session and then become a Scottish Law Lord.

Mark Napier was educated at Edinburgh High School and the University of Edinburgh. He would become the Sheriff of Dumfries and Galloway.

10 – There were a number of Edinburgh riots. The one in his mind here is the Porteous Riot 1736 where the prisoner, the captain of the city guard, was dragged from the prison and hung from a lamppost by a crowd of 4000. The place of the hanging is now marked by a plaque in the Grass-

---

[176] Atlay, 1899. Famous trials of the Century, page 113.
[177] Biographical sketch by Marjory Roy in Edinburgh geological society issue No.34.

market. Walter Scott's book, 'The Heart of Midlothian', is based on the story.

11 – The Skeleton of Bowed Joseph is one of the iconic items in the Anatomical Museum. He could raise a mob of 10,000 within a few hours with his drumming through the streets of Edinburgh. He did so on several occasions when he felt that the town council were not indulging in 'fair play'. He died after falling from a carriage and breaking his neck whilst returning from a day at Musselburgh Races in 1780.

12 – The entire court proceedings are available in a transcript written by John MacNee and published by Buchanan (1829). All sentences in speech marks in this chapter are direct quotes.

13 – The original court papers at the National Records of Scotland includes the original list of witnesses with handwritten notes in the margin as to what each one was going to add to the proceedings.[178]

14 – It appears in almost all biographies so it either happened or was reported in an early version of the story and has been retold by others.

15 - According to Roughhead (1948)[179], Hare informed the Edinburgh Evening Courant that John Broggan had hit the woman and killed her. Was he trying to shift the blame onto Broggan so that he and Burke could continue their business?

---

[178] List of witnesses cited. AD 2/1/3. National Records of Scotland.
[179] Roughead, 1948. Burke and Hare, page 43.

Notes on Chapter 15 – The Final Drop

1 - What happened to Burke after his death is well documented and appears in most biographies. It is detailed at the end of this notes section.

2 – Burkes' diet was changed from the standard bread and water in that last month on the advice of his physician[180].

3 – The suicide threat is mentioned in some of the earliest books.[181]

4 – This is a direct quote from Burke's interviews.

5 – This interview appeared in the Caledonian Mercury January 1829 and also appears in MacGregor (1884).[182]

6 – There is speculation at the beginning of MacGregors' book (MacGregor 1884) that Burke and Hare drugged their victims using laudanum. This method was later used by the 'London Burkers' whose actions pushed through the Anatomy Act 1832. If that has been the case why did Burke not confess that now rather than insisting that all the victims were suffocated?

7 – There is a letter from a priest in Ireland to an Edinburgh gentleman stating that Burke's wife knew about the proceedings against her husband[183].

---

[180] London Standard 26th January 1829. Caledonian Mercury at that time both available at the National Library of Scotland. Ireland 1829. West Port Murders, page 211.
[181] MacGregor, 1884. The history of Burke and Hare and of the resurrectionist times. Adams,1972. Dead and buried: The horrible history of bodysnatching, page 99.
[182] MacGregor, 1884. The history of Burke and Hare and of the resurrectionist times, page 278.
[183] MacGregor, 1884. The history of Burke and Hare and of the resurrectionist times, Appendix.

8 – This was refused on the grounds that the Lord Advocate thought a second confession that clashed with the one given to the Sheriff would cause issues.

The Letter to the Lord Provost reads:-

"Your Lordship is perhaps not aware that on the 3d instant, Burke intimated to the Sheriff, through the Governor of the jail, that being harassed by inquiries, he wished once for all to make a full confession of everything he could say in regard to the atrocious transactions in which he had been engaged, to the end that he might afterwards be allowed to remain unobstructed and apply his mind to things filled to his situation. In consequence of this communication, the Sheriff on that same day repaired to the jail and took down from Burke a full and voluntary confession which was drawn up in the shape of the declaration consisting of 19 pages. This declaration, is now in my possession, and I some time ago sent a copy of it to the Secretary of State.

It appears to me of importance both to the individual himself, and to the public, that no second statement, which might be contradictory or, or inconsistent with, the first (so solemnly and deliberately given) ought now to be impetrated from this man by irresponsible parties with a vowed object of its publication; and the proper answer for your Lordship in return is that Burke having himself most properly already selected such a mode of making his confession as was best calculated to secure its accuracy and to render it truly authentic, no deviation from that mode of proceeding can now be sanctioned, but that the Sheriff wait upon Burke, for the purpose of reading over to him the confession made of the 3d current, and that that magistrate will then take down whatever additions or alterations Burke may desire him to make upon it."

9 – Tracing this prisoner Ewart would be further confirmation that the Courant confession is a genuine document. If Burke handed him the confession then it is safe to assume that Burke thought he had a way of getting it out of the prison, maybe he was about to be released. If the prison

records of that time are searched then one possible match is found. Andrew Ewart was tried for murder and discharging a loaded gun on 11th February 1828. He was sentenced to hanging but the jury recommended mercy and so his sentence was amended to 12 months imprisonment. This provides a prisoner Ewart, a fellow murderer, about to be released in a prison in Edinburgh in January 1829. Could this be our man? We can begin to understand why Ewart betrayed Burke if we look a little further into the Ewart case. The jury had recommended mercy as Ewart had been a member of the watch tower team in Liberton cemetery. There had been an attempted grave robbing the week before and so they had started patrolling the cemetery at night. One of the team had been in the cemetery for a long time so, thinking that he may have encountered someone, Andrew Ewart and Henry Pennycook set off to find him. Rather than setting off together they departed separately, and in opposite directions. This led to the unhappy circumstance in which Henry failed to identify himself to Andrew and got shot. The case report at the time implies that all parties were in a state on intoxication and that Henry was 'frisking about among the grave-stones for the purpose of frightening the watch-men.'[184]

Andrew then found himself faced with the death penalty, commuted to 12 months imprisonment for trying to stop the supply of bodies to the anatomists. We could anticipate that he would not be sympathetic to helping Burke.

10 – This note has not been found but a note written on the same day – possibly part of the same note, is currently held by the New York Academy of medicine. A transcript of this note is in the chapter labelled 'The Third Confession' on page 187

11 – People are surprised by the fact that Burke could read and write. He was a well-educated man for his position. The court transcripts are very clear that he signed his name and that his wife was illiterate. If the signature is his then it is fair to assume the whole letter was written by

---

[184] Trial and Sentence 1828 Ry.III.a.2(83) National Records of Scotland.

him given the similarity in the writing.

12 – The Courant confession was published on the same day as the official confession. Mr Smith took proceedings out against the Courant arguing that the confession should have come to him. Both parties agreed to publish the confession when it became apparent that the official confession was about to be published and their document would become worthless.

13 – Burke had said he would not accept a pardon[185]. He was probably fairly confident that a pardon would not come as any hope of it had been crushed in the summary of the case by the judges. Some religious people chose to believe that he thought that he should not be pardoned for the crimes he had committed. They probably credited him with more of a conscience than he had.

14 – The only words that Burke spoke on the scaffold, quoted in nearly all the books[186].

[185] Leighton, 1861. The Court of Cacus, page 187.
[186] Douglas,1972. Burke and Hare :The true story, page 123, MacGregor, 1884. The history of Burke and Hare and of the resurrectionist times. Knight, 2007. Burke and Hare, page 93. Leighton, 1861. The Court of Cacus, page 196, Conaghan and Pickering, 2009. Burke and Hare, page 46. Adam, 1972. Dead and buried: The horrible history of bodysnatching, page 99.

After Burke's Death

His body was cut down after fifty minutes and placed in the city lock up. It lay there until the next day as there was fear that removing it to the University dissecting rooms whilst there was still a crowd present might have caused a commotion and the loss of the body.

On Thursday, January 29th 1829 it was taken to the dissecting rooms of the College of Medicine which were then in the old college building at the corner of Chambers Street and West College Street. Here it was examined by Alexander Monro 'tertius'. Mr Liston, Mr George Combe, Sir William Hamilton and Mr Samuel Joseph, a sculptor. The sculptor took a cast for a bust and presumably at this point the death mask was made.

It is thought that the investigation was limited to the brain, and yet the translated medical report covers other areas of his anatomy. The upper part of the cranium was removed and apparently a large amount of blood gushed out onto the floor

The Tunnel under the University that Burke's body would have travelled through.

which was not uncommon for someone who had been hanged. At this point Monro dipped his pen into the blood and wrote a statement onto a piece of paper[187].

Around 2.30 in the afternoon, the college quad was filled with students who were insisting that they should be admitted to see the remains. For around two hours there was a pitched battle with the police, wounded being removed from each side. Eventually, just after 4pm, Dr Christison appealed to the students arranging for them to be admitted into the room in groups of 50. On hearing this, the crowd of the general public who had gathered outside the University gates started to complain and they were only dispersed when it was agreed the body would go on general display the following day.

On Friday, January 30th, the doors opened at 10am and people started to trail past the naked body laying in state on the black marble slab. The crowd passed at around 60 people per minute and when the doors shut that evening it was estimated that 25,000 - 30,000 had trailed past the body, the same number as had seen him hanged. There was still a crowd waiting for admission and they returned the next day but to no avail.

Of the 30,000 spectators, 7 or 8 of them had been women. Leighton (1861) suggests that they might have been pulled in with the crowd and had not intended to view the body. Whatever their reason for being in the room, they were treated roughly by the male participants, as though their presence was not appropriate.

At some point a medical examination of the body must have taken place as a section of the report, compiled by Miller, in Latin, can be found within Thomas Stones' paper 1829. It is translated in a later section of this book.

Leighton tells us the body was then quartered, salted and preserved in barrels, with sections of the skin being removed to make souvenirs. Some skin sections were stolen from the dissecting room.[188] The skin of the neck being tanned brown and made into a tobacco-doss whilst the

---

[187] This piece of paper if held in the Centre for Research Collections at Edinburgh University. Figure 5 Page 154.
[188] Gordon, 2009. Burke and Hare: serial killers and resurrectionists of nineteenth century Edinbnurgh, page 177.

skin of the arm was tanned white and portraits of Burke and his wife and Hare being printed onto it. This was given to Mr Fraser, a jeweller, noted antiquarian and collector of curiosities. Both of these artefacts have disappeared, if they ever existed in the first place. There is also a notebook that is currently housed at Surgeons' Hall Museum and a calling card case held by the Cadies and Witchery Tours of Edinburgh. Both of these items are accompanied by documentation although they are not mentioned in Leighton's book[189].

A further section of skins with documents dating back to the period is being held in Stirling at the Smith art gallery and museum.

---

[189] The calling card case was sold by the family of Piercy Hughes, a descendant of one of the surgeons involved in the dissection.

The original indictment can be accessed at the National Records of Scotland in Edinburgh. AD 2/1/3.

The Indictment

1. William Burke and Helen M'Dougal, both present prisoners in the tollbooth of Edinburgh, you are both and each of you indicted and accused at the instance of Sir William Rae of St Catherine's, baronet, his majesty's advocate for his majesty's interest: that albeit by the laws of this and of every other well governed realm, murder is a crime of a heinous nature, and severely punishable, yet true it is and of verity that you the said William Burke and Helen M'Dougal are both and each, or one or other of you guilty of the said crime, actors or actor, or art and part: in so far as, on one or other of the days between the 7th and the 16th days of April,1828, or on one or other of the days of that month, or of March, immediately preceding, or of May immediately following, within the house in Gibbs close, Canon gate, Edinburgh, then or now or lately in the occupation of Constantine Burke, then or now or lately scavenger in the employment of the Edinburgh police establishment, you the said William Burke did wickedly and feloniously place or lay your body or person, or part thereof, over or upon the breast, or person, and face of Mary Paterson or Mitchell, then, or recently before that time, or formerly, residing with Isabella Burnet or Worthington, then or now or lately residing in Leith street, in or near Edinburgh, when she, the said Mary Paterson or Mitchell was lying in the said house in a state of intoxication, and did, by the pressure thereof, and by covering her mouth and nose with your body or person, and forcibly compressing her throat with your hands, and forcibly keeping her down, notwithstanding her resistance, or in some other way to the prosecutor unknown, preventing her from breathing, suffocate or strangle her; and the said Mary Paterson or Mitchell was this by the said means, or part thereof, or by some other means or violence, the particulars of which are to the prosecutor unknown, wickedly bereaved of life, and murdered by you the said William Burke: and this you did with

the wicked a forethought intent of disposing of, or selling the body of the said Mary Paterson or Mitchell, when so murdered, to a physician or surgeon, or some person in the employment of a physician or surgeon, as a subject for dissection, or with some other wicked and felonious intent or purpose to the prosecutor unknown.

2. Further, on one or other of the days between the 5th and 26th of October 1828, or on one or other of the days of that month, or the September immediately preceding, or the November immediate following, within the house situated in Tanners close, Portsburgh, or Wester Portsburgh, in or near Edinburgh, then or now or lately in the occupation of William Hairs or Hare, then or now or lately labourer, you the said William Burke did wickedly and feloniously attack and assault James Wilson, commonly called or known by the name daft Jamie, then or now or lately residing in the house of James Downie, then or now or lately residing in Stevenlaws' close, High Street Edinburgh, and did leap or throw yourself upon him, when the said James Wilson was lying in the said house, and he having sprung up you did struggle with him and did bring him to the ground, and you did place or lay your body or person or part thereof, over or upon the person or body and face of the said James Wilson , and did, but the pressure thereof, and by covering his mouth and nose with your person of body, and forcibly keeping him down, and compressing his mouth, nose and throat, notwithstanding every resistance on his part, and thereby, or in some manner to the prosecutor unknown, preventing him from breathing, suffocate or strangle him: and the said James Wilson was thus, by the said means, or part thereof, or by some other means or violence, the particulars of which are to the prosecutor unknown, wickedly bereaved of life and murdered by you the said William Burke; and this you did with the wicked afore thought intent (the intent specified in the same language as under the first minor charge)

3. Further on Friday the 31st day of October, 1828, or on one or other days of that month, or of September immediately preceding, or of November, immediate following, within the house then or lately occupied by you

the said William Burke, situated in that street of Portsburgh or Wester Portsburgh, in or near Edinburgh which runs from the Grassmarket of Edinburgh to Main Point, in or near Edinburgh, and on the north side of the said street, and having an access thereto by a trance or passage entering from the street last above libelled, and having also an entrance from a court or back court on the north thereof, the name of which is to the prosecutor unknown, you the said William Burke and Helen M'Dougal did, both and each, or one or the other of you, wickedly and feloniously place or lay your bodies or persons, or part thereof, or the body or person, or part thereof, of one or other of you, over or upon the person or body and face of Madgy or Margery, or Mary M'Gonegal or Duffie, or Campbell, or Docherty, then or lately residing in the house of Roderick Stewart or Steuart, then or now or lately labourer and then or now or lately residing in the Pleasance, in or near Edinburgh, when she the said Madgy, or Margery, or Mary M'Gonegal or Duffie, or Campbell or Docherty, was lying on the ground, and did , by the pressure thereof, and by covering her mouth and the rest of her face with your bodies or persons, or the body or persons of one or other of you, and by grasping her by the throat, and keeping her mouth and nostrils shut with your hands, and then, in some way to the prosecutor unknown, preventing her from breathing, suffocate or strangle her; and the said Madgy or Margery, or Mary M'Gonegal or Duffie, or Campbell or Docherty, was thus by the said means, or part thereof, or by some other means of violence, the particulars of which are to the prosecutor unknown, wickedly bereaved of life, and murdered by you the said William Burke and you the said Helen M'Dougal, or one or other of you, and this you both and each, or one or other of you, did with the wicked aforethought intent -(the intent specified in the same language as under the first and second minor charges). And you the said William Burke, having been taken before George Tait, Esq., sheriff-substitute of the shire of Edinburgh, you did, in his presence, emit and subscribe five several declarations, of the dates respectively following, viz. ; the 3rd, 10th, 19th and 29th days of November, and 4th day is December, 1828; and you the said Helen M'Dougal having been taken before the said sheriff-substitute, you did, in his presence at Edinburgh, emit two several declarations, one upon the 3rd, and another upon the 10th days of November, 1828; which declarations were each of them respectively subscribed in your presence by the said sheriff-substitute, you having declared you could not write: which declarations having to be used in evidence against each of you by whom the same were respectively emitted; as also the skirt of a gown, as also a petticoat, as also a snuff-box, and a snuff-spoon; a black coat, a black waistcoat, a pair of moleskin trowsers, and a cotton handkerchief or neckcloth, to all of which sealed labels are now attached, being to be used in evidence against you the said William Burke; as also a coarse linen sheet, a coarse pillow-case, a dark printed cotton gown, a red striped bed-gown, to which a sealed label in now attached; as also a wooden box; as also a plan entitled 'plan of houses in Wester Portsburgh and places adjacent', and bearing to be dated 'Edinburgh 20th November 1828' and to be signed by James Braidwood, 22, Society; being all used in evidence against both and each of you the said William Burke and Helen M'Dougal, at your trail, will, for that purpose, be in due time lodged in the hands of the Clerk of the High Court of justiciary, before which you are to be tried, that you may have an opportunity of seeing the same; all which, or part thereof, being found proven by the verdict of an assize or admitted by the respective judicial confessions of the said William Burke and Helen M'Dougal, before the Lord Justice-General, Lord Justice-Clerk, and Lords Commissioners of Justiciary - you, the said William Burke and Helen M'Dougal ought to be punished with the pains of the law, to deter others from committing the like crimes in all times coming.

The Official Confession

Printed in the Edinburgh Advertiser on 3 January 1829 – no official documentation survives.

Present - Mr George Tait, Sheriff-Substitute; Mr. Archibald Scott, Procurator-Fiscal; Mr. Richard J. Moxey, Assistant Sheriff-Clerk

Edinburgh, 3d January 1829

Compeared William Burke, at present under sentence of death in the jail of Edinburgh states that he never saw Hare till the Hallow-fair before last (November 1827), when he and Helen M'Dougal met Hare's wife, with whom he was previously acquainted, on the street; they had a dram, and he mentioned he had an intention to go to the West Country to endeavour to get employment as a cobbler; but Hare's wife suggested that they had a small room in their house which might suit him and M'Dougal, and that he might follow his trade of a cobbler in Edinburgh; and he went to Hare's house, and continued to live there, and got employment as a cobbler.

An old pensioner, named Donald, lived in the house about Christmas 1827; he was in bad health, and died a short time before his quarter's pension was due: that he owed Hare £4; and a day or two after the pensioner's death, Hare proposed that his body should be sold to the doctors, and that the declarant should get a share of the price. Declarant said it would be impossible to do it, because the man would be coming in with the coffin immediately; but after the body was put into the coffin and the lid was nailed down, Hare started the lid with a chisel, and he and the declarant took out the corpse and concealed it in the bed, and put tanner's bark from behind the house into the coffin, and covered it with a sheet, and nailed down the lid of the coffin, and the coffin was then carried away for interment. That Hare did not appear to have been concerned in anything of this kind before, and seemed to be at a loss how to get the body disposed of; and he and Hare went in the evening to the yard of the College, and saw a person like a student there, and the declarant asked him if there were any of Dr. Monro's men about, because he did not know there was any other way of disposing of a dead body - nor did Hare. The young man asked what they wanted with Dr. Monro, and the declarant told him he had a subject to dispose of, and the young man referred him to Dr. Knox, No. 10 Surgeons' Square; and they went there, and saw young gentlemen, who he now knows to be Jones, Miller and Ferguson, and told them that they had a subject to dispose of, but they did not ask how they had obtained it; and they told the declarant and Hare to come back when it was dark, and that they themselves would find a porter to carry it. Declarant and Hare went home and put the body into a sack, and carried it to Surgeons' Square, and not knowing how to dispose of it, laid it down at the door of the cellar, and they went up to the room, where the three young men saw them, and told them to bring up the body to the room, which they did; and they took the body out of the sack, and laid it on the dissecting table. That the shirt was on the body, but the young men asked no questions as to that; and the declarant and Hare, at their desire, took off the shirt, and got £7 10s. Dr. Knox came in after the shirt was taken off, and looked at the body, and proposed they should get £7 10s., and authorised Jones to settle with them; and he asked no questions as to how the body had been obtained. Hare got £4 5s. And the declarant got £3 5s. Jones & c., said that they would be glad to see them again when they had any other body to dispose of.

Early last spring, 1828, a woman from Gilmerton came to Hare's house as a nightly lodger,- Hare keeping seven beds for lodgers: That she was a stranger, and she and Hare became merry, and drank together; and next morning she was very ill In consequence of what she had got, and she sent for more drink, and she and Hare drank together, and she became very sick and vomited; and at that time she had not risen from bed, and Hare then said that they would try and smother her in order to

185

dispose of her body to the doctors: that she was lying on her back in the bed, and quite insensible from drink, and Hare clapped his hand on her mouth and nose, and the declarant laid himself across her body, in order to prevent her making any disturbances - and she never stirred; and they took her out of bed and undressed her, and put her into a chest; and they mentioned to Dr. Knox's young men that they had another subject, and Mr. Miller sent a porter to meet them in the evening at the back of the Castle; and declarant and Hare carried the chest till they met the porter, and they accompanied the porter with the chest to Dr. Knox's class-room, and Dr. Knox came in when they were there: the body was cold and stuff. Dr. Knox approved of its being so fresh, but he did not ask any questions.

The next was a man named Joseph, a miller who had been lying badly in the house: that he got some drink from declarant and Hare, but was not tipsy: he was very ill, lying in bed, and could not speak sometimes, and there was a report on that account that there was fever in the house, which made Hare and his wife uneasy in case it should keep away lodgers, and they (declarant and Hare) agreed they should suffocate him for the same purpose; and the declarant got a small pillow and laid it across Joseph's mouth; and Hare lay across the body to keep down the arms and legs; and he was disposes of in the same manner, to the same persons, and the body was carried by the porter who carried the last body.

In May, 1828, as he thinks, an old woman came to the house as a lodger, and she was the worse for drink, and she got more drink of her own accord, and she became very drunk, and declarant suffocated her; and Hare was not in the house at the time; and she was disposed of in the same manner.

Soon afterwards an Englishman lodged there for some nights, and was ill of the jaundice: that he was in bed very unwell, and Hare and declarant got above him and held him down, and by holding his mouth suffocated him, and disposed of him in the same manner.

Shortly afterwards an old woman named Haldane, (but he knows nothing farther of her) lodged in the house, and she got some drink at the time, and got more to intoxicate her, and he and Hare suffocated her, and disposed of her in the same manner. Soon afterwards a cinder woman came to the house as a lodger, as he believes, and got drink from Hare and the declarant, and became tipsy, and she was half asleep, and he and Hare suffocated her, and disposed of her in the same manner.

About Midsummer 1828, a woman, with her son or grandson, about twelve years of age, who seemed to be weak in the mind, came to the house as lodgers; the woman got a dram, and when in bed asleep, he and Hare suffocated her: and the boy was sitting at the fire in the kitchen, and he and Hare took hold of him, and carried him into the room, and suffocated him. They were put in a herring barrel the same night, and carried to Dr. Knox's rooms.

That, soon afterwards, the declarant brought a woman to the house as a lodger; and after some days she got drunk, and was disposed of in the same manner: that declarant and Hare generally tried if lodgers would drink, and if they would drink, they were disposed of in that manner.

The declarant then went for a few days to the house of Helen M'Dougal's father, and when he returned he learned from Hare that he had disposed of a woman in the declarant's absence, in the same manner, in his house; but the declarant does not know the woman's name, or any farther particulars of the case, or whether any other persons was present or knew of it.

That was about this time he went to live In Broggan's house, and a woman, named Margaret Haldane, daughter of the woman Haldane before mentioned, and whose sister is married to Clark, a tin smith in the High Street, came into the house, but the declarant does not remember for what purpose; and she got drink, and was disposed of in the same manner: That Hare was not present, and neither Broggan nor his son knew the least thing about that or any other case of the same kind.

That in April, 1828, he fell in with the girl Paterson and her companion in Constantine Burke's house, and they had breakfast together, and he sent for Hare, and he and Hare disposed of her in the same manner; and Mr. Ferguson and a tall lad, who seemed to have known the woman by sight, asked where they had got the body; and the declarant said he had purchased it from an old woman at the back of the Canongate. The body was disposed of five or six hours after the girl was killed, and it was cold, but not very stiff, but he does not recollect or any remarks being made about the body being warm.

One day in September or October 1828, a washer-woman had been washing in the house for some time, and he and Hare suffocated her, and disposed of her in the same manner.

Soon afterwards, a woman named M'Dougal, who was a distant relation of Helen M'Dougal's first husband, came to Broggan's house to see M'Dougal; and after she had been coming and going to the house for a few days, she got drink, and was served in the same way by the declarant and Hare.

That 'Daft Jamie' was then disposed of in that manner mentioned in the indictment, except that Hare was concerned in it. That Hare was lying along-side of Jamie in the bed, and Hare suddenly turned on him, and put his hand on his mouth and nose; and Jamie, who had got drink, but was not drunk, made a terrible resistance, and he and Hare fell from the bed together, Hare still keeping hold of Jamie's mouth and nose; and as they lay on the floor together, declarant lay across Jamie, to prevent him from resisting, and they held him in that state till he was dead, and he was disposed of in the same manner: and Hare took a brass snuff-box and a spoon from Jamie's pocket; and kept the box to himself, and never gave it to the declarant - but he gave him the spoon.

And the last was the old woman Docherty, for whose murder he has been convicted. That she was not put to death in the manner deponed to by Hare on the trial. That during the scuffle between him and Hare, in the course of which he was nearly strangled by Hare, Docherty had crept among the straw, and after the scuffle was over, they had some drink, and after that they both went forward to where the woman was lying sleeping, and Hare went forward first, and seized her by the mouth and nose, as on former occasions; and at the same time the declarant lay across her, and she had no opportunity of making any noise; and before she was dead, one or other of them, he does not recollect which, took hold of her by the throat. That while he and Hare were struggling, which was a real scuffle, M'Dougal opened the door of the apartment, and went into the inner passage and knocked at the door, and called out police and murder, but soon came back; and at the same time Hare's wife called out never to mind, because the declarant and Hare would not hurt one another. That whenever he and Hare rose and went towards the straw where Docherty was lying, M'Dougal and Hare's wife, who, he thinks, were lying in the bed at the time, or, perhaps, were at the fire, immediately rose and left the house, but did not make any noise, so far as he heard, and he was surprised at their going out at the time, because he did not see how they could have any suspicion of what they (the declarant and Hare) intended doing. That he cannot say whether he and Hare would have killed Docherty or not, if the woman had remained, because they were so determined to kill the woman, the drink being in their head;- and he has no knowledge or suspicion of Docherty's body having been offered to any person beside Dr. Knox; and he does not suspect that Paterson would offer the body to any other person than Dr. Knox.

Declares, that suffocation was not suggested to them by any person as a mode of killing, but occurred to Hare not he first occasion before mentioned, and was continued afterwards because it was effectual, and showed no marks; and when they lay across the body at the same time, that was not suggested to them by any person, for they never spoke to any person on such a subject; and it was not done for the purpose of preventing the person from breathing, but was only done for the purpose of keeping down the person's arms and thighs, to prevent the person struggling.

Declares, that with the exception of the body of Docherty, they never took the person by the throat, and they never leapt upon them; and declares that there were no marks of violence on any of the subjects, and they were sufficiently cold to prevent any suspicion on the part of the Doctors; and, at all events, they might be cold and stiff enough before the box was opened up, and he and Hare always told some story of their having purchased the subjects from some relation or other person who had the means of disposing of them, and about different parts of town, and the statements which they made were such as to prevent the Doctors having any suspicions; and no suspicions were expressed by Dr. Knox or any of his assistants, and no questions asked tending to show that they had suspicion.

Declares, that Helen M'Dougal and Hare's wife were no way concerned in any of the murders, and neither of them knew of anything of the kind being intended, even in the case of Docherty; and although these two women may latterly have had some suspicion in they own minds that the declarant and Hare were concerned in lifting dead bodies, he does not think they could have any suspicions that he and Hare were concerned in committing murders.

Declares, that none of the subject which they procured, as before mentioned, were offered to any other person than Dr. Knox's assistants, and he and Hare had very little communication with Dr. Knox himself; and declares, that he has not the smallest suspicion of any other person in this, or in any other country, except Hare and himself, being concerned in killing persons and offering their bodies for dissection; and he never knew or heard of such a thing having been done before.

Wm Burke
G Tait

Hare gave the same account as Burke of the number, and the same description of the victims; but they differ in the order of time in which the murders were committed. He stated, with great probability, that the body of Joseph the miller, was the second sold (that of the old pensioner being the first), and, of lucre he was the first man murdered. Burke, with less likelihood, asserts, as above, that the first murder was that of the female lodger. We are apt to think that Hare was right; for there was an additional motive to reconcile them to the deed in the miller's case - the fear that the apprehensions entertained through fever would discredit the house, and the consideration that there was, as they might ink, less crime in killing a man who was to die at any rate. It is not odd that Burke acted upon, as he seems always to have been, by ardent spirits, and involved in a constant succession of murder, should have misdated the two actions - original note by Sir Walter Scott.

Present - Mr. George Tait, Sheriff-Substitute; Mr Archibald Scott, Procurator-Fiscal; Mr Richard J. Moxey, Assistant-Sheriff-Clerk; the Rev. William Reid, Roman Catholic Priest

Edinburgh, 22d January 1829

Compeared William Burke, at present under sentence of death in the goal of Edinburgh, and his declaration, of date 3d current, being read over to him, he adheres thereto. Declares further, that he does not know the names and descriptions of any of the persons who were destroyed except as mentioned in his former declaration. Declares that he never was concerned in any other act of the same kind, nor made any attempt or preparation to commit such, and all reports of a contrary tendency, some of which he has heard, are groundless. And he does not know of Hare being concerned in any such, except as mentioned in his former declaration; and he does not know of any person being murdered for the purpose of dissection by any other persons than himself and Hare, and if any persons have disappeared anywhere in Scotland, England or Ireland, he knows nothing whatever about it, and never heard of such a thing till he was apprehended. Declares, that he never had any instrument in his house except a common table knife, or a knife used by him in his trade as a shoemaker, or a small pocket knife, and he never used any of those instruments, or attempted to do so, on any of the persons who were destroyed. Declares, that neither be not Hare, so far as he knows, ever were concerned in supplying any subjects for dissection except those before mentioned; and, in particular, never did so by raising bodies from the grave. Declares, that they never allowed Dr. Knox or any of his assistants, to know exactly where their houses were, but Paterson, Dr. Knox's porter or door-keeper, knew. And this he declares to be truth.

Wm. Burke
G. Tait

The 'Courant' Confession

Published in the Edinburgh Evening Courant on 7 February 1829 – no official documentation survives.

Abigail Simpson was murdered on the 12th February, 1828, on the forenoon of the day. She resided in Gilmerton, near Edinburgh; has a daughter living there. She used to sell salt and cam stone. She was decoyed in by Hare and his wife on the afternoon of the 11th February, and he gave her some whisky to drink. She had one shilling and sixpence, and a can of kitchen-fee. Hare's wife gave her one shilling and six pence for it; she drank it all with them. She then said she had a daughter. Hare said he was a single man, and would marry her, and get all the money amongst them. They then proposed to her to stay all night, which she did, as she was so drunk she could not go home; and in the morning was vomiting. They then gave her some porter and whisky, and made her so drink that she fell asleep on the bed. Hare then laid hold of her mouth and nose, and prevented her from breathing. Burke held her hands and feet till she was dead. She made very little resistance, and when it was convenient they carried her to Dr. Knox's dissecting-rooms in Surgeons' Square, and got ten pounds for her. She had on a drab ,angle, a white-grounded croon shawl and small blue sports on it. Hare took all her clothes and went out with them; said he was going to put them into the canal. She said she was a pensioner of Sir John Hay's. (Perhaps this should be Sir John Hope.)

The next was an Englishman, a native of Cheshire, and a lodger of Hare's. They murdered him in the same manner as the other. He was ill with the jaundice at the same time. He was very tall; had black hair, brown whiskers, mixed with grey hairs. He used to sell slinks in Edinburgh; was about forty years of age. Did not know his name. Sold to Dr. Knox for £10.

The next was an old woman who lodges with Hare for one night, but does not know her name. She was murdered in the same manner as above. Sold to Dr. Knox for £10. The old woman was decoyed into the house by Mrs. Hare in the forenoon from the street when Hare was working on the boats at the canal. She gave her whisky, and put her to bed three times. At last she was so drunk that she fell asleep; and when Hare came home to his dinner, he out part of the bed-tick on her mouth and nose, and when he came home at night she was dead. Burke was at this time mending shoes; and Hare and Burke took the clothes off her, and put her body into a tea-box. Took her to Knox's that night.

The next was Mary Paterson, who was murdered in Burke's brother's house in the Canongate, in the month of April last, by Burke and Hare, in the forenoon. She was put into a tea-box, and carried to Dr. Knox's dissecting-rooms in the afternoon of the same day; and got £8 for her body. She had two pence halfpenny, which she held fast in her hand. Declares that the girl Paterson was only four hours dead till she was in Knox's dissecting-rooms; but she was not dissected at that time, for she was three months in whisky before she was dissected. She was warm when Burke cut the hair off her head; and Knox brought a Mr. , a painter, to look at her, she was so handsome a figure, and well-shaped in body and limbs. One of the students said she was like a girl he has seen in the Canongate as one pea is like to another. They desired Burke to cut off her hair; one of the students gave a pair of scissors for that purpose.

In June last, an old woman and a dumb boy, her grandson, from Glasgow, came to Hare's, and both were murdered at the dead hour of night, when the woman was in bed. Burke and Hare murdered her the same way as they did the others. They took off the bed clothes and tick, stripped off her clothes, and laid her on the bottom of the bed, and then put on the bedrock, and bed clothes on the top of her; and they then came and took the boy in their arms and carried him in to the room, and murdered him in the same manner, and laid him alongside of his grandmother. They lay for the space of an hour; they then put them into a herring barrel. The barrel was perfectly dry; there was no brine in it. They carried them to the stable till next day; they put the barrel into Hare's cart, and

Hare's horse was yoked in it; but the horse would not drag the cart one foot past the meal market; and they got a porter with a hurley, and put the barrel on it. Hare and the porter went to Surgeons' Square with it. Burke went before them, as he was afraid something would happen, as the horse would not draw them. When they came to Dr. Knox's dissecting-rooms, Burke carried the barrel in his arms. The students and them had hard work to get them out, being so stiff and cold. They received £16 for them both. Hare was taken in by the horse he bought that refused drawing the corpse to Surgeons' Square, and they shot it in the tan-yard. He had two large holes in his shoulder stuffed with cotton, and covered over with a piece of another horse's skin to prevent them being discovered.

Joseph, the miller by trade, and a lodger of Hare's. He had once been possessed of a good deal of money. He was connected by marriage with some of the Carron Company. Burke and Hare murdered him by pressing a pillow on his mouth and nose till he was dead. He was then carried to Dr. Knox's in Surgeons' Square. They got £10 for him.

Burke and Helen M'Dougal were on a visit seeing their friends near Falkirk. This was at the time a procession was made round a stone in that neighbourhood; thinks it was the anniversary of the battle of Bannock-burn. When he was away, Hare fell in with a woman drunk in the streets at the West Port. He took her into his house and murdered her himself, and sold her to Dr. Knox's assistants for £8. When Burke went away he knew Hare was in want of money; his things were all in pawn; but when he came back, found him have plenty of money. Burke asked him if he had been doing any business, he said he had been doing nothing. Burke did not believe him, and went to Dr. Knox, who told him that Hare had brought a subject. Had then confessed what he and done.

A cinder-gatherer; Burke thinks her name was Effy. She was in the habit of selling small pieces of leather to him (as he was a cobbler), she gathered about the coach-works. He took her into Hare's stable, and gave her whisky to drink till she was drunk; she then lay down among some straw and fell asleep. They then laid a cloth over her. Burke and Hare murdered her as they did the others. She was then carried to Dr. Knox's, Surgeons' Square, and sold for £10.

Andrew Williamson, a policeman, and his neighbour, were dragging a drunk woman to the West Port watch-house. They found her sitting on a stair. Burke said "Let the woman go to her lodgings." They said they did not know where she lodged. Burke than said he would take her to her lodgings. They then gave her to his charge. He then took her to Hare's house. Burke and Hare murdered her that night the same way as they did the others. They carried her to Dr. Knox's in Surgeons' Square, and got £10.

Burke being asked, did the policeman know him when they gave him the drunk woman into his charge? He said he had a good character with the police; or if they had known that there were four murderers living in one house they would have visited them oftener.

James Wilson, commonly called Daft Jamie. Hare's wife brought him in from the street into her house. Burke was at the time getting a dram in Rymer's shop. He saw her take Jamie off the street, bare-headed and bare-footed. After she got him into her house, and left him with Hare, she came to Rymer's shop for a penny worth of butter, and Burke was standing at the counter. She asked him for a dram; and in drinking it she stamped him on the foot. He knew immediately what she wanted him for, and he then went after her. When in the house, she said, you have come too late, for the drink is all done; and Jamie had the cup in his hand. He had never seen him before to his knowledge. They then proposed to send for another half mutchkin, which they did, and urged him to drink; she took a little with them. They then invited him ben to the little room, and advised him to sit down upon the bed. Hare's wife then went out, and locked the outer door, and put the key below the door. There were none in the room but themselves three. Jamie sat down upon the bed. He then lay down upon the bed, and Hare lay down at his back, his head raised up and resting upon his left hand. Burke was standing at the fireside of the bed. When they had lain there for some time, Hare threw his body onto of Jamie, pressed his hand on his mouth, and held his nose with his other.

Hare and him fell off the bed and struggled. Burke then held his hands and feet. They never quitted their gripe till he was dead. He never got up nor cried any. When he was dead, Hare felt his pockets, and took out a brass snuff-box and a copper snuff-spoon. He gave the spoon to Burke, and kept the box to himself. Sometime after, he said he threw the box away in the tan-yard; and the brass-box that was libelled against Burke in the Sheriff's-office was Burke's own box. It was after breakfast that Jamie was enticed in, and he was murdered by twelve o'clock in the day. Burke declares that Mrs. Hare led poor Jamie in as a dumb lamb to the slaughter, and as a sheep to the shearers; and he was always very anxious making inquiries for his mother, and was told she would be there immediately. He does not think that he drunk above one glass of whisky all the time. He was then out into a chest that Hare kept clothes in; and they carried him to Dr. Knox's in Surgeons' Square, that afternoon, and got £10 for him. Burke gave Daft Jamie's clothes to his brother's children; they were almost naked; and when he untied the bundle they were like to quarrel about them. The clothes of the other murdered persons were generally destroyed, to prevent detection.

Ann M'Dougal, a cousin of Helen M'Dougal's former husband. She was a young woman, and married, and had come on a visit to see them. Hare and Burke gave her whisky till she was drunk, and when in bed and asleep, Burke told Hare that he would have most to do to her, as she being a distant friend; he did not like to begin first on her. Hare murdered her by stopping her breath, and Burke assisted him the same way as the others. One of Dr. Knox's assistants, Paterson, gave them a fine trunk to put her into. It was in the afternoon when she was done. It was in John Broggan's house; and when Broggan came home from his work he saw the trunk, and made inquiries about it, as he knew they had no trunks there. Burke than gave him two or three drama, as there was always plenty of whisky going at these times, to make him quiet. Hare and Burke then gave him £1 10s. each, as he was back in his rent, for to pay it, and he left Edinburgh a few days after. They then carried her to Surgeons' Square as soon as Broggan went out of the house, and got £10 for her. Hare was cautioner for Broggan's rent, being £3, and Hare and Burke gave him that sum. Broggan went off in a few days, and the rent is not paid yet. They gave him the money that he might not come against them for the murder of Ann M'Dougal, that he saw in the trunk, that was mustered in his house. Hare thought that the rent would fall upon him, and if he could get Burke to pay half of it, it would be so much the better; and proposed this to Burke, and he agreed to it, as they were glad to get him out of the way. Broggan's wife is a cousin of Burke's. They thought he went to Glasgow, but are not sure.

Mrs. Haldane, a stout woman, who had a daughter, transported last summer from the Calton jail for fourteen years, and had another daughter married to , in the High Street. She was a lodger of Hare's. She went into Hare's stable; the door was left open, and she being drunk, and falling asleep among some straw, Hare and Burke murdered her the same way as they did the others, and kept the body all night in the stable, and took her to Dr. Knox's the next day. She had but one tooth in her mouth, and that was a very large one in front. A young woman, a daughter of Mrs. Haldane, of the name of Peggy Haldane, was drunk and sleeping in Broggan's house, was murdered by Burke himself, in the forenoon. Hare had no hand in it. She was taken to Dr. Knox's in the afternoon in a tea-box, and £8 got for her. She was so drunk at the time that he thinks she was not sensible of her death, as she made no resistance whatever. She and her mother were both lodgers of Hare's and they were both of idle habits, and much given to drinking. This was the only murder that Burke committed by himself, but what Hare was connected with. She was laid with her face downwards, and he pressed her down, and she was soon suffocated.

There was a Mrs. Hostler washing in John Broggan's, and she came back next day to finish up the clothes, and when done, Hare and Burke gave her some whisky to drink, which made her dunk. This was in the day-time. She then went to bed. Mrs. Broggan was out at the time. Hare and Burke murdered her the same way they did the others, and put her in a box, and set her in the coal house in the passage, and carried her off to

Dr.knox's in the afternoon of the same day, and got £8 for her. Broggan's wife was out of the house at the time the murder was committed. Mrs. Hostler had ninepence halfpenny in her hand, which they could scarcely get out of it after she was dead, so firmly was it grasped.

The woman Campbell or Docherty was murdered on the 31st October last, and she was the last one. Burke declares that Hare perjured himself on his trial. When giving evidence against him, as the woman Campbell or Docherty lay down among some straw at the bedside, and Hare laid hold of her mouth and nose, and pressed her throat, and Burke assisted him in it, till she was dead. Hare was not sitting on a chair at the time, as he said in the Court. There were seven shillings in the woman's pocket, which they divided between Hare and Burke.

That was the whole of them - sixteen in whole: nine murdered in Hare's house, and four in John Broggan's; two in Hare's stable and one in Burke's brother's house in the Canongate. Burke declares that five of them we're murdered in Hare's room that has the iron bolt in the inside of it. Burke did not know the days nor the months the different murders were committed, nor all their names. They were generally in a state of intoxication at those times, and paid little attention to them; but they were all from 12th February till 1st November, 1828; but he thinks Dr. Knox will know by the dates of paying him the money for them. He never was concerned with any other person but Hare in those matters, and was never a resurrection man, and never dealt in dead bodies but what he murdered. He was urged by Hare's wife to murder Helen M'Dougal, the woman he lived with. The plan was, that he was to go to the country for a few weeks, and then write to Hare that she had died and was buried, and he was to tell this to deceive the neighbours; but he would not agree to it. The reason was, they could not trust to her, as she was a scotch woman. Helen M'Dougal and Hare's wife were not present when those murders committed: they might have a suspicion of what was doing, but did not see them done. Hare was always the most anxious about them, and could sleep well at night after committing a murder; but Burke repented often of the crime, and could not sleep without a bottle of whisky by his bedside, and a two penny candle to burn all night beside him; when he awoke he would take a draught of the bottle -sometimes half a bottle at a draught - and that would make him sleep. They had a great many pointed out for murder, but were disappointed of them by some means or other; they were always in a drunken state when they committed those murders, and when they got the money for them while it lasted. When done, they would pawn their clothes, and would take them out as soon as they got a subject. When they first began this murdering system, they always took them to Knox's after dark; but being so successful, they went in the day-time, and grew more bold. When they carried the girl Paterson to Knox's, there were a great many boys in the High School Yards, who followed Burke and the man that carried her, crying, "They are carrying a corpse": but they got her safe delivered. They often said to one another that no person could find them out, no one being present at the murders but themselves two; and that they might be as well hanged for a sheep as a lamb. They made it their business to look out for persons to decoy into their houses to murder them. Burke declares, when they kept the mouth and nose shut a very few minutes, they could make no resistance, but would convulse and make a rumbling noise in their bellies for some time; after they ceased crying and making resistance, they left them to die of themselves; but their bodies would often move afterwards, and for some time they would have long breathings before life went away. Burke declares that's it was God's providence that put a stop to their murdering career, or he does not know how far they might have gone with it, even to attack people on the streets, as they were so successful, and always met with a ready market: that when they delivered a body they were always told to get more. Hare was always with him when he went with a subject, and also when he got the money. Burke declares, that Hare and him had a plan made up, that Burke and a man were to go to Glasgow or Ireland, and try the same there, and to forward them to Hare, and he was to give them to Dr. Knox. Hare's wife always got £1 of Burke's share, for the use of the house, of all that were murdered in their house; for if the price received was £10, Hare got £6, and Burke got only £4; but Burke did not give her the £1 for Daft Jamie for which Hare's wife would not speak to him for three weeks. They could get nothing done during the harvest-time, and also after harvest, as Hare's house was so full of lodgers. In Hare's house were eight beds for lodgers; they paid 3d. each; and two, and sometimes three, slept in a bed; and during harvest they gave up their own bed when throng. Burke declares they went under the name of resurrection men in the West Port, where they lived, but not murderers. When they wanted money, they would say they would go and look for a shot; that was the name they gave them when they wanted to murder any person. They entered into a contract with Dr. Knox and his assistants that they were to get £10 in winter and £8 in summer for as many subjects as they could bring to them.

Old Donald, a pensioner, who lodged in Hare's house, and died of a dropsy, was the first subject they sold. After he was put into the coffin and the lid put on, Hare unscrewed the nails and Burke lifted the body out. Hare filled the coffin with bark from the tan-yard, and put a sheet over the bark, and it was buried in the West Church Yard. The coffin was furnished by the parish. Hare and Burke took him to the College first; they saw a man there, and asked for Dr. Monro, or any of his men; the man asked what they wanted, or had they a subject; they said they had. He then ordered them to call at 10. Dr. Knox's in Surgeons' Square and he would take it from them, which they did. They got £7 10s. for him. That was the only subject they sold that they did not murder; and getting that high price made them try the murdering for subjects.

Burke is thirty-six years of age, was born in the parish of Orrey, county Tyrone; served seven years in the army, most of that time as an officer's servant in the Donegal militia; he was married at Ballinha, in the county of Mayo, when in the army, but left his wife and two children in Ireland. She would not come to Scotland with them. He had often wrote to her, but got no answers; he came to Scotland to work at the Union Canal, and wrought there while it lasted; he resided for about two years in Peebles, and worked as a labourer. He wrought as weaver for eighteen months, and as a baker for five months; he learned to mend shoes, as a cobbler, with a man he lodged with in Leith; and he has lived with Helen M'Dougal about ten years, until he and she were confined in Calton Jail, on the charge of murdering the woman of the name of Docherty or Campbell, and both were tried before the High Court of Justiciary in December last. Helen M'Dougal charge was found not proven, and Burke found guilty, and sentenced to suffer death on the 28th January.

Declares, that Hare's servant girl could give information respecting the murders done in Hare's house, if she likes. She came to him at Whitsunday last, went to harvest, and returned back to him when the harvest was over. She remained until he was confined along with his wife in the Calton Jail. She then sold twenty-one of his swine for £3, and absconded. She was gathering potatoes in a field that day Daft Jamie was murdered; she saw his clothes in the house when she came home at night. Her name is Elizabeth M'Guier or Mair. Their wives saw that people came into their houses at night, and went to bed as lodgers, but did not see them in the morning, nor did they make any inquiries after them. They certainly knew what became of them, although Burke and Hare pretended to the contrary. Hare's wife often helped Burke and Hare to pack the murdered bodies into the boxes. Helen M'Dougal never did, nor saw them done, Burke never durst let her know; he told her he bought dead bodies, and sold them to doctors, and that was the way they got the name of resurrection men.

Burk declares that doctor Knox never incoureged him, neither taught or incoregd him to murder any persons, neither any of his asistents, that worthy gentlemen Mr. Fergeson was the only man that ever mentioned anything about the bodies. He inquired where we got that young woman Paterson.

Signed. William Burk, prisoner Condemned Cell, January 21, 1829

The Third Confession

Handwritten note currently held by the New York Academy of Medicine.
http://nyam.contentdm.oclc.org/cdm/compundobject/collection/p133001coll2/id/470/rec/1

Dear Friend, I meant to mention to you somethings that I was accused for last concerning a snuff box that was supposed to be Daft Jameys. I take it to death with me that the snuff box that I had in the lock up and was after consigned to the Sheriff's Office is not Jameys box. It is my own, the spoon was Jameys. William Burk.

Next is was reported that I had doctors instruments in my house and that there was a letter found in my house seemingly from a doctor. Also declares it false and there was questions put to me concerning murders in England. I also declare I never was there nor knows nothing of them. As for the women in the canal or...... I never knew anything of it nor any of those people who has....

I gave the Sheriff an account of sixteen people who had been murdered by Hare and me which was all I ever had any hand in in all my life. William Burk.

Concerning Daft Jamey, I declare that William Hare was the first that laid hands on him. I never threatened to stab him with a knife and it was Hare's wife that brought him into the house. William Burk.

Figure 8 – hand written third confession

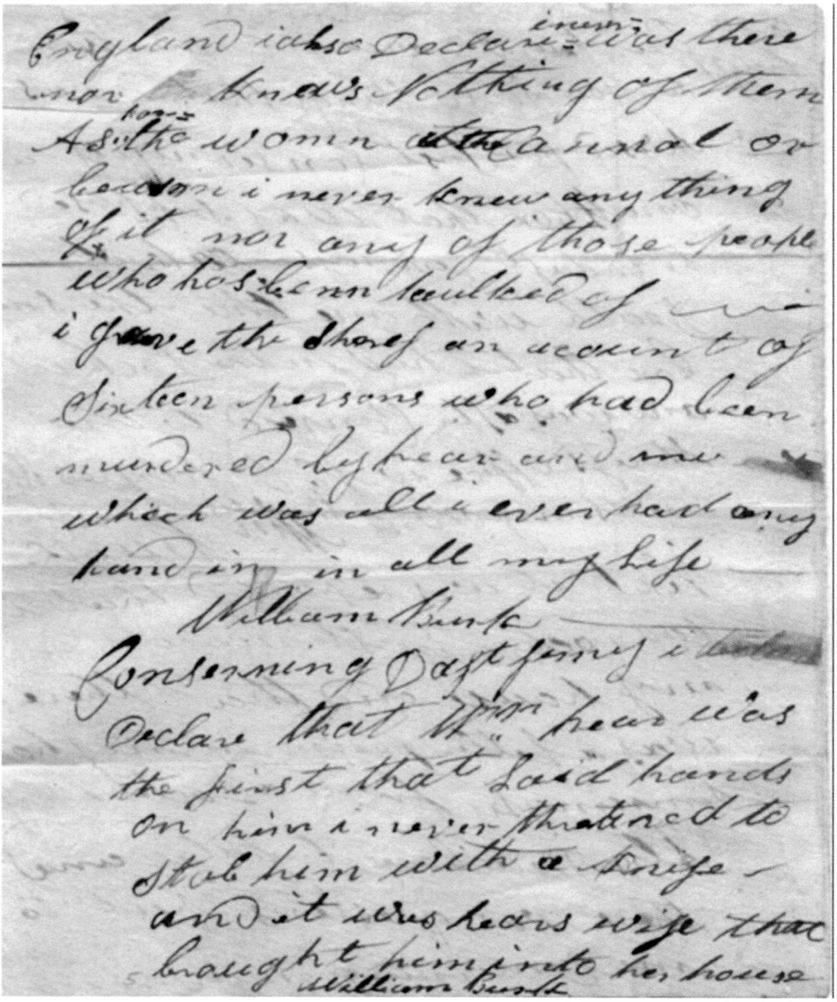

The Medical report – first published in Thomas Stones' paper 1829.

– translated by Felicity Loughlin – University of Edinburgh 2016

As we explored the corpse of this abominable murderer only one testicle appeared – which is worthy of note; for the other had been utterly
swallowed up by a disease with which it had been afflicted. That disease
appears to have been a scrofulous sore [*exulceratio scrophulosa*] of the
testicle, and I posited that there were some below [*et ea infra posui*],
which were found after death. The view of the exterior of the scrotum
from the left of the raphe at least in part was natural; from the right very
many sores indeed were seen, which were sinuous, so to speak, motion-
less [*inertia*]. These sores were greatly occupying that part of the scrotum, which, when the body is erect, lies near to the inner thigh, and even
that part between where the scrotum and thigh join. To a less attentive
observer, these sores seem only to be lying at the top of the skin, and do
not seem to penetrate the testicle itself deeply.

After they had been opened, however, and the external coverings
removed, a certain amount of fluid was discovered of a yellowish or
brownish colour, similar to that which was flowing out from the cavi-
ties [*sinibus*]. Having cut further, from the right hand side, not even the
smallest trace of the *Tunica vaginalis*, and *nothing of the testicle,* appeared; indeed the location of these was filled with a certain semi-fluid
substance, dark-coloured, not smelling in any peculiar way, similar to
meconium in some manner, yet not nearly as black. The seminal vesicles
[*Vesiculae seminales*] were larger than is customary, and contained a
brownish liquid. In many places the scrotal septum [*septum scroti*] had
been corroded and gradually for that reason, its blackish substances were
discovered also on the left side, up to the top part of the *tunica vaginalis*.
Even the membranes, both the adipose and cellulose, were filled with

the same substance, which covered over the accelerators of urine [*acceleratores urinae*]. From the left-hand side, the tunica vaginalis and the testicle were in the natural way, which at the laboratory, they rejoiced at the sight of; *but here the testicle was certainly smaller than usual,* and different in length, as is commonly the case, where the other testicle had been destroyed. The spermatic chord on either side was found to exceed the normal size.

Bibliography

Adams, Norman. 1972. *Dead and Buried: The horrible history of bodysnatching*. Bell.

Atlay, J.B. 1899. *Famous Trials of the Century*. Grant Richards (London).

Bailey, Brian. 2002. *Burke and Hare – the year of the ghouls*. Mainstream Publishing.

Byrd, Elizabeth. 1974. *Rest without peace*. Macmillian (London).

Buchanan, Robert. 1829. *The trial of William Burke and Helen M'Dougal, before the High Court of Justiciary at Edinburgh*. Shorthand by James MacNee.

Buchanan, Robert.(2) 1829. *Supplement to the trial of William Burke and Helen M'Dougal : containing the whole legal proceedings against William Hare, in order to bring him to trial for the murder of James Wilson, or Daft Jamie; with an appendix of curious and interesting information*. Shorthand by James MacNee.

Christison, Robert. 1829. *A Treatise on Poisons, in relation to medical jurisprudence, physiology and practice of physics*. Adam Black (Edinburgh).

Conaghan, Martin. and Pickering, Will. 2009. *Burke and Hare the graphic novel*. Transfuzion publishing.

Douglas, Hugh. 1973. *Burke and Hare: The true story*. Robert Hale (London).

Duff, Charles. 1954. *A new handbook on hanging; being a short introduction to the fine art of execution, containing much useful information on neck-breaking, throttling, strangling, asphyxiation, decapitation and electrocution*. Hale, Cushman and Flint.

Duff, Peter. 1999. *The Scottish Criminal Jury: a very peculiar institution in Law and Contemporary Problems*. Volume 62, No2, Page 173.

'Echo of Surgeons' Square'. 1829. *Letter to the Lord Advocate disclosing the accomplices, secrets and other facts relative to the late murders etc.* Menzies (Edinburgh)

Edwards, Owen Dudley. 1980. *The true story of the infamous Burke and Hare*. Polygon (Edinburgh).

Gordon, R. Michael. 2009. *Infamous Burke and Hare: serial Killers and resurrectionists of nineteenth century Edinburgh*. McFarland and Co.

Ireland, Thomas (publisher) 1829. *West Port Murders: or, an authentic account of the atrocious murders committed by Burke and his associates; containing a full account of all the extraordinary circumstances connected with them, also, a report of the trial of Burke and M'Dougal.* (Edinburgh).

Kaufman, Matthew. 1997. *Another look at Burke and Hare: the last days of Mary Paterson – a medical cover up?* Proceedings of the Royal College of Physicians of Edinburgh Issue 27, Pages 78-88.

Kaufman, Matthew. 2003. *Medical teaching in Edinburgh during the 18th and 19th centuries*. Royal College of Surgeons.

Kaufman, Matthew. 2005. Exhibition catalogue to commemorate the 300th Anniversary of the Chair of Anatomy in the University of Edinburgh 29th August 1705-2005.

Knight, Alana. 2007. *Burke and Hare*. Kew: the National Archives.

Leighton, Alexander. 1861. *The Court of Cacus or the story of Burke and Hare*. Houlston and Weight (Edinburgh).

Lonsdale, Henry. 1870. *A sketch of the life and writings of Robert Knox the anatomist*. Macmillian (London).

MacGregor, George. 1884. *The history of Burke and Hare and of the resurrectionist times*. Thos D. Morison (Glasgow).

MacKay, John. 2007. *The True Story of Burke and Hare*. Lang Syne Publishing.

Moore, Wendy. 2005. *The Knife Man: blood, bodysnatching and the birth of modern surgery*. Bantam Books.

Pentland, Gordon. 2008. *Radicalism, Reform and National Identity in Scotland 1820-1833. Royal Historical Society Studies in History*. Boydell Press, Woodbridge.

Rosner, Lisa. 2010. *The Anatomy Murders. Being the true and spectacular history of Edinburgh's notorious Burke and Hare and of the man of science who abetted them in the commission of their most heinous crimes*. University of Pennsylvania Press.

Roughead, William (ed.) 1948. *Burke and Hare*. Wm Hodge (Edinburgh).

Scott, Walter. 1818. *The Heart of Midlothian*.

Simpson, James. 1834. *Necessity of popular education as a national object: with hints on the treatment of criminals and observation on homicidal insanity*. Adam and Charles Black.

Stevenson, Robert Louis. 1884. *The Body Snatcher*. Pall Mall.

Stone, Thomas. 1829. *Observations on the phrenological development of Burke and Hare and other atrocious murderers*. Robert Buchanan (Edinburgh).

Struthers, John. 1867. *Historical Sketch of the Edinburgh Anatomical School*. Maclochlen and Stewart (Edinburgh).

Townsend, John. 2001. *Burke and Hare: the body snatchers*.

Watters, Brian. 1998. *Where iron runs like water! A new history of Carron Iron Works 1759-1982*. John Donald Publishers. ISBN 0859765059.

Wormersley, Tara and Crawford, Dorothy, H. 2010. *Body snatchers to lifesavers*. Luath Press.

Edinburgh City Archives

Magdalene Asylum Minutes 1825-1838 SL237/1/3

Committee Minute Book 1812-1823 SL 237/3/4

Minute Book of Subcomittee 1823-1834 SL 237/3/5

Lothian Health Service Archives – accessed by e mail request

Lothian Health Services General Register of Patients LHB1/126/51

National Library of Scotland

Trail and Sentence of Andrew Ewart

http://digital.nls.uk/broadsides/broadside.cfm/id/15493/transcript/1

Accessed May 2015.

AD14/28/13 and court minute book JC8/22, f.62r

Burks papers: a full copy of the curious papers which were found under a flag stone at the general cleaning of the city, near Burke's house, where you have the names of those who were murdered and sold by him. Together with the prices, and the sums received 1832 F.3.a.13(48) NLS

Burke and Hare: the resurrection men: a collection of contemporary documents including broadsides, occasional verses, illustrations polemics and a complete transcript of the testimony from the trial ; from the Fenwick Beekman Collection at New York Academy. Barzun, Jacques 1974 Q3.77.787 NLS

Edinburgh University Library.

Mic Dup 1316 Monro Alexander tertius ' Memorial to Burke and Hare the West Port Murders' 1828

An account of the last moments and execution of William Burke of Edinburgh for the West Port Murders

Buchanan, Robert. *Supplement to the trail of William Burke and Helen M'Dougal: containing the whole legal proceedings against William Hare, in order to bring him to trial for the murder of James Wilson, or Daft Jamie; with an appendix of curious and interesting information.* Shorthand by James MacNee. 1829

Centre for Research Colelctions. Edinburgh University. S.B.34352(4107) Bur.

Ireland, Thomas. *West Port Murders: or, an authentic account of the atrocious murders committed by Burke and his associates; containing a full account of all the extraordinary circumstances connected with them, also, a report of the trial of Burke and M'Dougal.* 1829 RB.S.347

MacGregor, George. *History of Burke and Hare and the resurrectionist times; a fragment from the criminal annals of Scotland*. Thos. D.Morrison (Glasgow). 1884. Zv.6.26 Centre for Research Collections. Edinburgh University

Smith, William. *Laconic narrative of the life and death of James Wilson, known by the name of Daft Jamie: in which are interspersed, several anecdotes relative to him and his old friend Boby Awl, an idiot who strolled about Edinburgh for many years.* 1881 S.B.9(41445)092 Smi

National Records of Scotland

Printed indictment against Burke and Helen McDougal detailing the charges against them, namely the murders of Mary Paterson or Mitchell, James Wilson and Madgy McGonnegal, and lists the witnesses cited AD2/1/3

High Court Book of Adjournal containing the record of Burke and McDougal's trail JC4/18

High Court Minute Book containing the records of Burke and McDougal's trail JC8/23

High Court Book of Adjournal containing the record of processing concerning a petition for a bill of avocation and suspension and liberation for Hare Jan-Feb 1829 JC4/19

High Court minute Book containing the record of procedures concerning a petition for a bill of avocation and suspension and liberation for Hare Jan-Feb 1829 JC8/23

Petition by Archibold Scott, procurator-fiscal to the Sheriff of Edinburgh, for warrant to apprehend William Burke, shoemaker in Wester Portsburgh, near Edinburgh, Helen McDougal, there, William Hare, labourer, there and Margaret Laird, his wife, for the murder of Mysie or Madgy McGonnegal or Campbell or Duffy from Ireland, 3 November 1828 GD1/353/3

Petition by Archibold Scott, procurator-fiscal to the Sheriff of Edinburgh, for warrant to apprehend William Burke, shoemaker in Wester Portsburgh, near Edinburgh, Helen McDougal, there, William Hare, labourer, there and Margaret Laird, his wife, for the murder of James Wilson, High

Street, Edinburgh 19 November 1828 GD1/353/4

Petition by Archibold Scott, procurator-fiscal to the Sheriff of Edinburgh, for warrant to apprehend William Burke, shoemaker in Wester Portsburgh, near Edinburgh, Helen McDougal for the murder of Mary Paterson alias Mitchell, 4 December 1828 GD1/353/5

Prison records for Edinburgh Lock Up house in November 1828 HH21/8/1

National Archives of the United Kingdom

Donegal Militia Muster Books and Pay lists

WO 13/2761 1808

WO 13/2762 1809

WO 13/2763 1810-1811

because no one should have to wait
188 years
to be checked for cancer...